Standards-Based Assessment Resource

Grade 4

Houghton Mifflin Harcourt

10 (b) Credit: U.S. Air Force photo by Master Sgt. Bill Huntington; 21 (t) ©Alan Schein/Alamy Images; 21 (t) Terraxplorer/Getty Images; 21 (b) © Nikreates / Alamy; 23 (t) ©jeancliclac/iStockPhoto.com; 23 (b) Nick White/Digital Vision/Getty Images; 25 (t) ©LexussK/iStockphoto.com/Getty Images; 25 (t) ©Ilene MacDonald/Alamy Images; 25 (b) ©Lloyd Sutton/Alamy; 37 (b) ©Pierre Arsenault/Radius Images/Getty Images; 80 (t) ©piboon/Fotolia

Printed in the U.S.A.

ISBN 978-0-544-59326-8

10   0982   23 22 21 20 19 18

4500695712   D E F G

Contents

Overview

Assessments and Performance Tasks

As you use the Houghton Mifflin Harcourt *Journeys* instructional program, you have a rich array of materials to foster students' achievement week by week and unit by unit. The *Standards-Based Assessment Resource* includes Assessments and Performance Tasks that align with the content in *Journeys* and give students practice with the high-stakes tests they will encounter. Rigorous tasks and questions, complex text, and technology-enhanced item formats (online only) prepare students for success on standards-based assessments. At the end of each unit, you can use an Assessment or Performance Task to obtain a broader picture of achievement.

Assessments

The Assessments can be given three times a year, at the end of Units 1, 3, and 5. These tests are cumulative. The Unit 1 Assessment draws from Unit 1, while the Units 3 and 5 Assessments draw upon skills that have been taught in the current and previous units. The item types and assessment formats presented are the same kinds that students will encounter on high-stakes tests and provide essential practice in test-taking strategies.

Each Assessment has four sections. The Reading section assesses comprehension and vocabulary strategies. The Writing section draws upon the grammar, spelling, and writing skills taught to date. The Listening section presents audio or read-aloud passages that assess the listening skills that students will encounter on high-stakes tests. The Research section assesses a combination of comprehension, research/media literacy, and writing skills.

The Listening section of the Assessments includes a source that students must listen to and then answer questions about. The source will not be available as text to students. If you administer a paper-and-pencil version of the Assessments, you will read the source aloud to students. If you administer the online Assessment, students will need to access audio on a computer.

Performance Tasks

The Performance Tasks can also be given three times a year, at the end of Units 2, 4, and 6. Each Performance Task draws upon the reading, writing, and research skills taught in the current and previous units. These tasks encourage students to integrate knowledge and skills to conduct complex analysis and research.

A brief Classroom Activity will be conducted prior to each Performance Task to orient students to the context of the task. The Classroom Activity includes a summary of one source from the Performance Task and prompts for a classroom discussion. At the end of the Classroom Activity, the teacher will be directed to make a brief statement that explains the purpose of the activity within the context of the Performance Task as a whole.

Each Performance Task features two parts. Part 1 introduces a group of related text sources. Students should be encouraged to take notes as they read the sources. After the sources, students will encounter a set of questions related to the passage. The answers to the items will be scored. Part 2 introduces the essay prompt, along with a brief description of the scoring criteria. The essay will be scored using one of three rubrics.

General Guidelines for Administering

The Assessments and Performance Tasks are group-administered and may be taken online or as a paper-and-pencil version. At Kindergarten and Grade 1, some sections of the tests are read aloud. These sections are noted in the specific guidelines for administering the tests. At Grade 2 and beyond, students can read the directions and take the tests independently. At all grades, the Listening section of the Assessments and the Classroom Activity of the Performance Tasks will be administered by the teacher.

Test Time

The Assessments are not timed. The Performance Tasks have suggested completion times listed on the teacher overview pages.

Allowable Resources

Students may access several resources while they complete the Assessments and Performance Tasks.

> **Pen/pencil/highlighter and blank/lined paper:** Students are encouraged to take notes throughout the Performance Tasks, and they may choose to take notes as they complete the Assessments.

> **Hard-copy dictionary:** Students are allowed to access dictionaries as they write the essay during Part 2 of the Performance Task.

> **Headphones:** All students will need headphones to complete the Listening section of each online Assessment.

Item Types

The Assessments and the Performance Tasks include the following item types:

- Selected-response items: These multiple-choice items require students to choose an answer from several provided options. Some items will require students to select multiple correct options.

- Constructed-response items: These items require students to write or type a response.

- Interactive items: Interactive items require students to complete a table or underline a portion of the text. Interactive items online require students to interact with the text by clicking cells in a table or highlighting a portion of text.

Guidelines for Administering Assessment 1

Use the following directions as you administer each section.

Reading, Writing, and Research

Students will read the passages and stimuli independently, and then they will complete the corresponding items.

Listening

The Listening prompts are below for read-aloud presentation.

Say: *Listen to the presentation. Then answer the questions about the presentation.*

History and Harlem

Harlem is part of New York City. It is also part of American history. The Harlem Renaissance took place during the 1920s and 1930s. It was a time of new energy and ideas in the arts. Many African American poets, novelists, and other writers lived in Harlem in those days. There were many artists and musicians, too.

Money was scarce, so many people held parties! Each guest paid a small fee for admission, which would help pay the host's rent. Today, tourists visit some of the blocks of apartments where now-famous people once worked and worried.

One gift to America from Harlem was jazz, the first truly American music. The Savoy Ballroom featured jazz bands, singers, and dancers. Dancers at the Savoy invented many popular dances of the 1920s. Another good place to hear jazz was the Cotton Club. The Savoy and the Cotton Club are gone now, but another music landmark, the Apollo Theater, still stands.

Say: *Listen to the presentation. Then answer the questions about the presentation.*

Toe Shoes and Tutus

Ballet began in Italy in the 1400s. Catherine de Medici brought it to France in the mid-1500s after she married King Henry II. Over the next 400 years, ballet thrived in France, beginning with a dance school opening in 1661. Ballets started appearing in theaters, and their audiences grew quickly. Even today, all the ballet positions, steps, and jumps have French names.

Russia began to lead the ballet world at the end of the 1800s with composers who wrote music just for ballets. Russian dance companies toured the globe in the early 1900s, inspiring dancers everywhere.

Today, many countries have ballet companies and ballet schools. It takes years to train to do all the steps to perfection and in time with the music and the other dancers. A ballet might tell a story or evoke an idea or an emotion. The dancers leap and turn and spin in the air. The audience applauds the dancers, music, costumes, and stage sets.

Say: *Listen to the presentation. Then answer the questions about the presentation.*

Protecting Valuable Resources

Every day, you use products made from trees, such as wood, paper, and cloth. But trees are valuable for much more than their products.

Trees add to the health and beauty of our environment, help cool buildings, and can even make neighborhoods more pleasant. Trees provide shade and block wind. They are sources of food and shelter for animals, and they help reduce water pollution.

Trees are also a source of jobs. Trees have to be planted and cared for. Some trees are cut down, and a distributor hauls them to a lumber mill, where machines turn the timber into boards, chips, and pulp. After that, workers distribute the lumber and its products to other businesses. For each of these jobs, other workers have to make and sell supplies and equipment.

Because trees are such valuable resources, we must be careful not to use too many of them. People must work together to keep planting new trees and to protect our forests.

Guidelines for Administering Performance Task 1

Animals and Their Unique Abilities

Classroom Activity *(20 minutes)*

1. Allow students to independently read "Desert Birds." This article focuses on animal adaptation and specifically on how birds adapt to survive in the desert. The article describes different types of birds, the desert environment in which they live, and how these birds survive in such a unique place.

2. Lead a brief class discussion about the article, using the questions below.

   Question 1: How do birds adapt to survive in the desert? How do key details in the article help explain this main idea?

   Question 2: What are some reasons that adaptation is helpful for birds?

3. Explain that students will use this article and two other articles to write a narrative about animals with unique abilities for other students and teachers.

Student Task Overview

Part 1 *(55 minutes)*

Students will examine the additional stimuli independently and will take notes. They will then respond to constructed-response and selected-response items.

Part 2 *(45 minutes)*

Students will continue to have access to the sources they utilized in the Classroom Activity and Part 1. They will refer to their notes and their answers to the items to write a narrative. They will prewrite, draft, and revise that narrative. The narrative created at the end of Part 2 will be scored. Reading notes from Part 1 and prewriting and drafting from Part 2 will not be scored.

Task Specifications and Scoring Rubrics

Review the REMEMBER section at the end of the student performance task to remind students about the elements of a well-written narrative.

Score student responses using the Performance Task: Narrative Writing Rubric.

Guidelines for Administering Assessment 2

Use the following directions as you administer each section.

Reading, Writing, and Research

Students will read the passages and stimuli independently, and then they will complete the corresponding items.

Listening

The Listening prompts are below for read-aloud presentation.

Say: *Listen to the presentation. Then answer the questions about the presentation.*

The Return of the Wolf

For thousands of years, wolf packs traveled throughout most of North America. Today, however, wolves can be found in only eight states. When settlers and farmers moved into the West, wolves became a problem. Ranchers began to kill the wolves to protect their cattle and sheep.

By 1930, not many wolves were left. They could be found in only a few places. In fact, wolves had disappeared from every state except Alaska!

In recent years, several states have tried to bring the wolf back into their wilderness areas. Some programs release wolves that have been raised in zoos. By living together as pups, the wolves form bonds. After the wolves are released, scientists hope they survive by forming packs with other wolves and hunting on their own.

The United States government also put wolves on the endangered species list. This meant that nobody could hunt wolves. The government designated areas of wilderness off-limits to businesses, ranchers, and city development.

One important area where wolves are recovering is Yellowstone National Park in Wyoming. About 100 wolves now live and hunt there.

Say: *Listen to the presentation. Then answer the questions about the presentation.*

When Tsunamis Strike

A tsunami is a set of large ocean waves. It is caused by water being moved or pushed rapidly. Tsunamis are caused by movements in Earth's outermost layer. They can be caused by earthquakes, landslides, and volcanoes. In an earthquake, a giant wave of water is pushed away from the starting point. These powerful waves can become tsunamis. In a landslide, the Earth's outermost layer splits. Huge chunks of rock slide deep into the ocean. Large amounts of water are pushed out of place. When a volcano under the ocean erupts, this also causes powerful waves.

A tsunami starts by moving outward from the starting point of an earthquake or another great force. In deep open water, it can move between 500 and 600 miles per hour. Where the water is deep, tsunami waves are not very tall.

However, as the waves get closer to land, they slow down and become taller. Because of their great height, some tsunamis are powerful enough to move cars and large boats. They can even destroy large buildings.

Say: *Listen to the presentation. Then answer the questions about the presentation.*

Butterflies

Butterflies in the lycaenid family are unique. Lycaenid butterflies feed on plants so that they can attract their enemies, the ants.

The butterflies begin by laying their eggs in the flowers. Then, the eggs hatch and caterpillars come out. They chew on the flowers to grow. Later, the caterpillars use a silk thread to reach the ground. They secrete a sweet liquid and wait for red ants to adopt them. If the red ants taste the liquid and approve, the caterpillars are carried back to the ants' larvae chamber. The caterpillars exchange their sweet liquid for food and protection from the ants.

After three to four weeks, the caterpillars turn into butterflies. They must escape the ant nest. As they leave, ants try to kill them! The ants no longer recognize these butterflies as the caterpillars they had cared for.

Not all caterpillars that have been adopted by ants will survive as butterflies. But even fewer caterpillars survive as butterflies if they are not adopted by ants.

Guidelines for Administering Performance Task 2

Earth's Changing Climate

Classroom Activity *(20 minutes)*

1. Allow students to independently read "Earth's Climate Cycles." This article focuses on the natural changes Earth's climate has experienced over time.

2. Lead a brief class discussion about the passage using the questions below.

   Question 1: What are some of the causes of climate change?

   Question 2: What do you imagine happens to Earth as the climate changes?

3. Explain that students will use this article and two others to develop and write an opinion essay about climate change and animal adaptation for other students and teachers.

Student Task Overview

Part 1 *(55 minutes)*

Students will examine the additional stimuli independently and will take notes. They will then respond to constructed-response and selected-response items.

Part 2 *(45 minutes)*

Students will continue to have access to the sources they used in the Classroom Activity and Part 1. They will refer to their notes and their answers to the items to write an opinion essay. The report created at the end of Part 2 will be scored. Reading notes and answers to the items in Part 1 and prewriting and drafting in Part 2 will not be scored.

Task Specifications and Scoring Rubrics

Review the REMEMBER section at the end of the student performance task to remind students about the elements of a well-written opinion essay.

Score student responses using the Performance Task: Opinion Writing Rubric.

Guidelines for Administering Assessment 3

Use the following directions as you administer each section.

Reading, Writing, and Research

Students will read the passages and stimuli independently, and then they will complete the corresponding items.

Listening

The Listening prompts are below for read-aloud presentation.

Say: *Listen to the presentation. Then answer the questions about the presentation.*

Earthquakes

You are reading when you feel your room start to shake. Earthquake! The shaking lasts only a few seconds, but it feels much longer. You wonder, "What causes earthquakes, anyway?"

The crust is the outermost layer of Earth. It is broken up into large pieces called plates. The plates are constantly moving, usually very slowly. As the plates push against one another, a tremendous amount of stress, or pressure, is put on the rocks beneath the surface. This stress causes the plates to suddenly shift and slide over, under, or past one another, and it also causes the rocks to break up.

When this happens, waves of energy travel from the broken rock throughout the surrounding area. These waves of energy are called seismic waves. Seismic waves occur because the energy from an earthquake has to go somewhere. The release of seismic waves causes a violent shaking of the earth.

Say: *Listen to the presentation. Then answer the questions about the presentation.*

Animal Collectors

Many people collect valuable items, but did you know that some animals are collectors, too?

One animal collector is the red squirrel. It gathers food to hide in a single tree hole, hollow log, or pile called a midden. The squirrel builds a midden by sitting in its favorite spot, eating nuts, seeds, and pinecones.

As the squirrel eats, bits of shells and pinecones fall to the ground and form a large pile. In the fall, the squirrel collects pinecones: It stores them deep in the pile. By the time winter comes, the squirrel has stored a lot of food.

The gray squirrel is a collector, too. However, it has a different system called scatter hoarding. The squirrel makes hundreds of small hiding places for its nuts and seeds. Even if another animal finds one of the hiding places, food in other areas will be safe. How does the squirrel find the food later? It cleans every seed and nut before storing it. Cleaning makes the food easier for the squirrel to smell and find later, even under a layer of snow!

Say: Listen to the presentation. Then answer the questions about the presentation.

Why Are Trees Valuable?

People have always depended on trees. For example, Native Americans tapped maple trees for syrup and ate fruits and nuts from trees. Later, settlers in America burned firewood for warmth and cooking. They built homes and furniture from wood, and they also used trees to build ships.

Today, trees continue to be a valuable resource. Think about all the products you use every day that are made from wood, paper, or other tree products.

Trees also contribute to the health and beauty of our environment. Even in crowded cities, planners make room for trees. This is because trees help cool buildings on a hot day, make neighborhoods more pleasant, and provide shade and block wind. They are a source of food and shelter for animals. They also help reduce water pollution.

Trees are even a source of jobs. Have you ever thought about how many people it takes to turn a tree in the forest into a board in your home? First, trees have to be planted and cared for, and then the trees are cut down and hauled to a lumber mill. There, machines turn the dried timber into boards. After that, more people take the lumber and its products to other businesses.

Guidelines for Administering Performance Task 3

Giving Others a Helping Hand

Classroom Activity *(20 minutes)*

1. Allow students to independently read "The Man Who Built Libraries." This historical article tells about the life of Andrew Carnegie and how he funded public libraries throughout the nation. It also includes a brief definition of the word *philanthropist*.

2. Lead a brief class discussion about the article, using the questions below.

   Question 1: What is a philanthropist? Why did Carnegie choose to become one? Do you think that was a good decision? Does the article encourage you to think that it was a good idea? How?

   Question 2: How did Carnegie's work affect communities? Why is this good?

3. Explain that students will use this article and two other articles to write an informative essay on how philanthropy, the process of helping others by giving time and money, can improve communities.

Student Task Overview

Part 1 *(55 minutes)*

Students will examine the additional stimuli independently and will take notes. They will then respond to constructed-response and selected-response items.

Part 2 *(45 minutes)*

Students will continue to have access to the sources they used in the Classroom Activity and Part 1. They will refer to their notes and answers to the items in Part 1 to write a report. They will prewrite, draft, and revise that report. The report created at the end of Part 2 will be scored. Reading notes from Part 1 and prewriting and drafting from Part 2 will not be scored.

Task Specifications and Scoring Rubrics

Review the REMEMBER section at the end of the student performance task to remind students about the elements of a well-written informative essay.

Score student responses using the Performance Task: Informative Writing Rubric.

Scoring and Interpreting the Results

Scoring

The answers to the Assessments and Performance Tasks can be found in the Answer Keys section. Each correct response to a selected-response item is worth one point. Each constructed-response item is worth two points. Constructed-response items and essay responses should be scored using the rubrics provided in this book. Sample answers to the constructed-response items are given on the Answer Key and should be used as a guide to score a student's responses. Because these questions require students to think deeply about comprehension, both the teacher and students can learn a great deal by discussing students' responses and their reasoning.

Duplicate a Test Record Form for each student and enter the scores in the Student Score column. This form will allow you to track a student's performance across the year. If you require a percentage score for each test to help in assigning grades, apply the formula in the optional Final Score row and record that score.

Interpreting

Consider each student's scores on the Test Record Form. Students who achieve an Acceptable Score (indicated on the form) or higher are most likely ready to move to the next unit in the book.

For struggling students, duplicate the Answer Key. Circle the item numbers answered incorrectly for each Assessment or Performance Task and compare the corresponding skills indicated. Look for patterns among the errors to help you decide which skills need reteaching and more practice.

Assessment 1

Item Number	Correct Answer	Unit, Lesson, Program Skill	Depth of Knowledge
		READING	
1	B	U1L3: Vocabulary Strategy: Using Context	2
2	C	U1L4: Comprehension: Theme	3
3	See answer below.	U1L5: Comprehension: Understanding Characters	3
	"We were worried…"; "We thought it …"; "As for us, we imagined that…"		
4	C	U1L4: Comprehension: Theme	3
5	B, F	U1L5: Comprehension: Understanding Characters	2
6	D	U1L4: Comprehension: Theme	3
7	A	U1L5: Comprehension: Understanding Characters	2
8	D; A	U1L4: Vocabulary Strategy: Prefixes *non-*, *mis-*	2
9	A	U1L5: Comprehension: Hyperbole	1
10	See rubric on p. T24.	U1L1: Comprehension: Point of View	4
	Sample two-point response: "The Mysterious Tree" is written in first person and "Growing a Patch of the Prairie" is in third person. The author used first person because it helps the reader know what the narrator and the other friends are thinking. For example, it starts by saying how the narrator feels about the town of Fernwood. The second story is in third person, so the author has to tell the reader what the characters are feeling by using words like "happily," "puzzled" and "with a smile."		
	Sample one-point response: "The Mysterious Tree" tells about a town written by a person who lives there. You can tell that because it says "I." "Growing a Patch of the Prairie" talks about two people who are neighbors, but it doesn't use "I." You don't know who is telling the story.		
11	C, E	U1L2: Comprehension: Author's Purpose	3
12	B; B	U1L3: Comprehension: Interpret Visuals	2
13	D	U1L3: Vocabulary Strategy: Using Context	2
14	They must be careful not…	U1L2: Comprehension: Author's Purpose	3
15	A	U1L1: Vocabulary Strategy: Prefixes *re-*, *un-*, *dis-*	2
16	illiterate	U1L2: Vocabulary Strategy: Prefixes: *in-*, *im-*, *il-*, *ir-*	3
17	D; A	U1L2: Comprehension: Idioms	2
18	D	U1L3: Comprehension: Cause and Effect	3
19	B, F	U1L5: Vocabulary Strategy: Reference Materials	3
20	See rubric on p. T24.	U1L3: Comprehension: Domain-Specific Vocabulary	3
	Sample two-point response: Dogs have intelligence. The second article says instinct means something you are born with. Dogs are not born with the rescue skill, so it is not an instinct. The first article says dogs have to spend hours training to learn the skill. They also sometimes have to do things without their trainer there so that means they must be able to think.		
	Sample one-point response: Dogs have intelligence because they can learn. Otherwise, they would not be able to be rescue dogs. Rescue dogs have to train and do things without their owners around.		

Item Number	Correct Answer	Unit, Lesson, Program Skill	Depth of Knowledge
WRITING			
21	B	U1L5: Spelling: Homophones	2
22	A	U1L3: Grammar: Quotations	1
23	The mayor in her blue car. A tall man with….	U1L4: Grammar: Fragments and Run-on Sentences	1
24	C	U1L2: Grammar: Kinds of Sentences	2
25	steemed, dich	U1L2: Spelling: Short *e* and Long *e*	1
26	C	U1L1: Writing: Elaboration	2
27	B, D	U1L1: Writing: Elaboration	2
28	A	U1L4: Writing: Organization	2
29	D	U1L4: Writing: Organization	2
30	See rubric on p. T24.	U1L1: Writing: Elaboration	3
	Sample two-point response: Joan watched the young man load her bags onto the cart. She liked the way he helped her up into the front seat. Soon they were heading down the road toward the school where Joan would work. All along the way there were neat farms. Crops were growing high in the fields. The road crossed over a stream. Nate told her funny stories and made her laugh. She was so happy that she felt as if her life were a dream.		
	Sample one-point response: Joan watched the young man load her bags onto the cart. Then they drove to the school where Joan would work. She thought that the trip seemed like a nice dream.		
LISTENING			
31	B	U1L4: Speaking and Listening: Draw and Support Conclusions	2
32	B	U1L4: Speaking and Listening: Draw and Support Conclusions	1
33	A, C	U1L4: Speaking and Listening: Draw and Support Conclusions	2
34	A	U1L4: Speaking and Listening: Draw and Support Conclusions	1
35	B; D	U1L4: Speaking and Listening: Draw and Support Conclusions	3
36	B	U1L4: Speaking and Listening: Draw and Support Conclusions	1
37	A, E	U1L4: Speaking and Listening: Draw and Support Conclusions	2
38	C	U1L4: Speaking and Listening: Draw and Support Conclusions	3
39	A; D	U1L4: Speaking and Listening: Draw and Support Conclusions	3
RESEARCH			
40	B, F	U1L2: Research and Media Literacy: Analyze Sources	2
41	See answer below.	U1L3: Research and Media Literacy: Use Evidence	2
	"Scientists have discovered…"; "Volunteering makes people…"		

Item Number	Correct Answer	Unit, Lesson, Program Skill	Depth of Knowledge
42	C	U1L3: Comprehension: Interpret Visuals	2
43	B, F	U1L3: Research and Media Literacy: Use Evidence	2
44	"He wanted Delta…"	U1L3: Research and Media Literacy: Use Evidence	2

Performance Task 1

Item Number	Correct Answer	Unit, Lesson, Program Skill	Depth of Knowledge
1	See rubric on p. T24.	U1L3: Research and Media Literacy: Use Evidence	3
	Sample two-point response: Whether it's living in hard conditions or defending themselves from enemies, animals use their unique abilities to adapt. Source #1 says that roadrunners have special glands to remove salt from their bodies. Source #2 says that an octopus will change colors in order to shock an enemy or to blend into the background to hide. The ability to change colors is the octopus's way to protect itself from enemies.		
	Sample one-point response: Animals use their unique abilities to adapt. Source #1 says sandgrouses can carry water to their babies using their feathers. Without this unique ability, the sandgrouse would not be able to help its babies survive.		
2	See rubric on p. T24.	U1L2: Research and Media Literacy: Analyze Sources	4
	Sample two-point response: Source #3 is the most helpful for understanding how an animal can be trained to use their unique abilities. The capuchin monkey is trained to use its skills to help people in wheelchairs. They can do tasks to help people in wheelchairs. This shows that they can use their unique ability to learn new and difficult tasks for different purposes. This source also says that these monkeys can learn simple commands.		
	Sample one-point response: Source #3 is the most helpful for understanding how an animal can be trained. The capuchin monkey is trained to use its skills to help people in wheelchairs. This shows that they can use their unique ability to learn new and difficult tasks for different purposes.		
3	See answer below.	U2L7: Research and Media Literacy: Locate Information from Text Source	3
	Some animals have developed special body features that help them adapt to their environment: Source #1 and Source #2. Animals can develop relationship with people: Source #3. Animals can communicate their emotions in different ways: Source #2.		
Essay Response	See rubric on p. T25.	U1L5: Writing: Narrative	4

Assessment 2

Item Number	Correct Answer	Unit, Lesson, Program Skill	Depth of Knowledge
		READING	
1	B; A	U2L8: Comprehension: Understanding Characters	3
2	C	U3L15: Vocabulary Strategy: Using Context	1
3	D	U3L12: Comprehension: Conclusions and Generalizations	3
4	"Break a leg!"	U2L9: Vocabulary Strategy: Figurative Language	2
5	See rubric on p. T24.	U2L9: Comprehension: Understanding Characters	3
5	Sample two-point response: Aisha decided to create her own sound effects when she realized that she could use the objects and people around her to create sound effects. She had been waiting for the computer to work and, while she was waiting, she heard the sounds going on around her.		
5	Sample one-point response: Aisha decided to create her own sound effects because she couldn't use the computer to download them.		
6	C, E	U2L7: Comprehension: Explain Concepts and Ideas	3
7	C	U3L15: Vocabulary Strategy: Using Context (Multiple-Meaning Words)	2
8	C; C	U3L11: Comprehension: Text and Graphic Features	3
9	A, E	U3L15: Comprehension: Analyze an Argument	3
10	A	U3L12: Vocabulary Strategy: Synonyms	2
11	C	U2L10: Comprehension: Simile and Metaphor	3
12	E-mail is much…	U3L15: Vocabulary Strategy: Using Context	3
13	D	U3L15: Comprehension: Main Idea and Details	2
14	See rubric on p. T24.	U3L14: Comprehension: Author's Purpose	4
14	Sample two-point response: The author's purpose in both articles is to inform. In both articles, the author is teaching the reader about the advancements in communication through the years, through mail and telephone. The author uses facts, dates, and information to teach the reader about the topics.		
14	Sample one-point response: The author's purpose is to inform in both articles.		
15	A	U3L11: Comprehension: Text Structure (Cause and Effect)	2
16	D	U3L15: Vocabulary Strategy: Using Context (Multiple-Meaning Words)	2
17	A; pleased, smiling, cheerful, smile	U2L8: Comprehension: Understanding Characters	3
18	B	U3L12: Comprehension: Conclusions and Generalizations	2
19	E, F	U2L9: Vocabulary Strategy: Antonyms	3
20	2, 5, 3, 1, 4	U3L12: Comprehension: Sequence of Events	2

Item Number	Correct Answer	Unit, Lesson, Program Skill	Depth of Knowledge
		WRITING	
21	too, vary	U3L11: Grammar: Frequently Confused Words	2
22	D	U3L15: Spelling: Changing Final *y* to *i*	1
23	nervusly	U2L8: Spelling: Vowel Sounds: /ou/	1
24	D	U2L6: Writing: Organization	2
25	C	U2L8: Grammar: Progressive Verb Tenses	1
26	C	U2L9: Grammar: Compound and Complex Sentences	2
27	B	U2L6: Writing: Organization	2
28	A, C	U2L6: Writing: Organization	2
29	D	U2L10: Writing: Elaboration	2
30	See rubric on p. T24.	U3L12: Writing: Organization	3
	Sample two-point response: There are many reasons to remove homework or lessen the amount of homework in schools. Too much homework can harm student health, take time away from other activities, and hinder student learning. Homework impacts the daily lives of students in a negative way.		
	Sample one-point response: There are many reasons to remove homework. Too much homework can harm student health and hinder student learning. Homework should not be assigned to students in schools.		
		LISTENING	
31	B, D	U2L10: Speaking and Listening: Identify and Interpret Purpose, Central Idea, and Key Points	1
32	B	U2L10: Speaking and Listening: Identify and Interpret Purpose, Central Idea, and Key Points	2
33	C	U3L13: Speaking and Listening: Draw and Support Conclusions	3
34	C; A	U3L13: Speaking and Listening: Draw and Support Conclusions	3
35	A, E	U2L10: Speaking and Listening: Identify and Interpret Purpose, Central Idea, and Key Points	2
36	A	U3L13: Speaking and Listening: Draw and Support Conclusions	3
37	D	U2L10: Speaking and Listening: Identify and Interpret Purpose, Central Idea, and Key Points	1
38	See answer below.	U2L10: Speaking and Listening: Identify and Interpret Purpose, Central Idea, and Key Points	1
	Chews flowers: Caterpillar; Carries insect back to nest: Ant; Uses silk thread: Caterpillar; Tastes sweet liquid: Ant; Turns into butterfly: Caterpillar		
39	D	U3L13: Speaking and Listening: Draw and Support Conclusions	2

Item Number	Correct Answer	Unit, Lesson, Program Skill	Depth of Knowledge
		RESEARCH	
40	Another type of…	U2L7: Research and Media Literacy: Locate Information from Text Source	2
41	Martin finished school…, After graduating from…	U3L14: Research and Media Literacy: Use Evidence	2
42	D	U3L11: Research and Media Literacy: Interpret Information from Visual Source	2
43	B, E	U2L7: Research and Media Literacy: Locate Information from Text Source	2
44	A, D	U3L14: Research and Media Literacy: Use Evidence	2

Performance Task 2

Item Number	Correct Answer	Unit, Lesson, Program Skill	Depth of Knowledge
1	See rubric on p. T24.	U3L11: Comprehension: Explain Scientific Ideas	3
	Sample two-point response: Source #2 explains that climate change can be harmful to various animals. For example, the temperature of the ocean can rise, which affects how corals get their food. Deadly diseases are also able to thrive in this warmer water.		
	Sample one-point response: Source #2 explains that the ocean water gets warmer as the climate changes.		
2	See rubric on p. T24.	U4L19: Research and Media Literacy: Interpret Information from Text Source	3
	Sample two-point response: Source #3 outlines how several animals are adapting to climate change. Butterflies move to higher areas where the temperatures are lower. Tawny owls are changing from white to brown.		
	Sample one-point response: Source #3 shows how animals adapt to climate change. It mentions that corals are adapting to warmer water.		
3	See answer below.	U3L14: Research and Media Literacy: Use Evidence	4
	Row 1: Source #1; Row 2: Sources #1 and #2; Row 3: Source #3		
Essay Response	See rubric on p. T27.	U3L15: Writing: Opinion	4

Assessment 3

Item Number	Correct Answer	Unit, Lesson, Program Skill	Depth of Knowledge
1	D	U5L21: Comprehension: Idioms	2
2	C	U4L18: Comprehension: Theme	2
3	D	U5L24: Vocabulary Strategy: Suffixes *-ed, -ly*	2
4	A, D	U4L18: Comprehension: Story Structure	3
5	See rubric on p. T24.	U4L16: Comprehension: Compare and Contrast	3
	Sample two-point response: In the beginning of the story, Kira felt disorganized and unsure of a solution to her problem. In the story, she talked to her mom and her friends about her problem. In the end of the story, Kira was happy. She felt like her problem had been solved and she was helping her friends at the same time.		
	Sample one-point response: Kira was unhappy at the beginning of the story because her mom wanted her to get rid of some books. She was happy at the end of the story because she had figured out a way to keep her books and to organize her collection.		
6	D	U5L22: Comprehension: Cause and Effect	2
7	D	U4L17: Comprehension: Sequence of Events	2
8	A	U5L23: Comprehension: Text Structure: Sequence	1
9	organization	U4L17: Vocabulary Strategy: Suffixes *–ion, –ation, –ition*	3
10	B; D	U4L19: Comprehension: Conclusions and Generalizations	3
11	D, E	U5L24: Comprehension: Fact and Opinion	3
12	D	U5L21: Vocabulary Strategy: Context: Multiple Meaning Words	2
13	A	U5L22: Vocabulary Strategy: Adages and Proverbs	3
14	A; B	U5L22: Comprehension: Domain-Specific Vocabulary	3
15	See rubric on p. T24.	U4L20: Comprehension: Main Idea and Details	4
	Sample two-point response: Eleanor Roosevelt was a woman of many strengths and accomplishments. The article says that she was active in the Red Cross, helped in the League of Women Voters, and had a daily newspaper column. She was also appointed by two presidents to serve on important committees. The article also states that no other First Lady of the United States has received as many awards and honors as she did.		
	Sample one-point response: Eleanor Roosevelt was an important First Lady. She made many contributions when she was First Lady, such as taking care of the president and having a radio show. She also worked for women's rights.		
16	C	U4L16: Comprehension: Personification	2
17	C, D	U5L25: Comprehension: Author's Purpose	2
18	excavated	U5L23: Vocabulary Strategy: Prefixes *pre–, inter–, ex–*	3
19	enormous, huge, vast	U4L20: Vocabulary Strategy: Shades of Meaning	3
20	D; B	U5L21: Comprehension: Point of View	3

Item Number	Correct Answer	Unit, Lesson, Program Skill	Depth of Knowledge
		WRITING	
21	A	U4L19: Spelling: Suffixes *–ful, –less, –ness, –ment*	1
22	A	U4L19: Grammar: Relative Pronouns and Adverbs	2
23	C	U4L18: Grammar: Prepositions and Prepositional Phrases	2
24	B, D, E	U4L18: Writing: Elaboration	2
25	B	U5L23: Writing: Organization	2
26	A	U5L22: Writing: Elaboration	1
27	D	U5L25: Writing: Elaboration	2
28	picnik, notise	U4L16: Spelling: Words with /k/	1
29	It was the warmer..., He had to leave...	U5L21: Grammar: Comparative and Superlative Adjectives and Adverbs	2
30	See rubric on p. T24.	U4L19: Writing: Organization	3
	Sample two-point response: After getting off the bus, I walked to room 27, my new classroom. I was nervous as I wondered who my new teacher would be. My heart was beating so fast I thought it might pound its way out of my chest. Finally, I got to room 27. The sign on the classroom door said, "Welcome to Mr. Harper's Class!" A huge smile grew across my face! Luis was in Mr. Harper's class last year, and I was hoping he would be my teacher, too.		
	Sample one-point response: I walked to room 27, my new classroom. My heart was beating so fast I thought it might pound its way out of my chest. I was nervous as I wondered who my new teacher would be. Luis was in Mr. Harper's class last year, and I was hoping he would be my teacher, too. The sign on the classroom door said, "Welcome to Mr. Harper's Class!" A huge smile grew across my face!		
		LISTENING	
31	D; C	U4L17: Speaking and Listening: Identify Ideas and Supporting Evidence	2
32	A, D	U4L17: Speaking and Listening: Identify Ideas and Supporting Evidence	3
33	C	U4L17: Speaking and Listening: Identify Ideas and Supporting Evidence	2
34	B	U4L17: Speaking and Listening: Identify Ideas and Supporting Evidence	2
35	B	U5L23: Speaking and Listening: Identify Ideas and Supporting Evidence	3
36	A; D	U5L23: Speaking and Listening: Identify Ideas and Supporting Evidence	1
37	A, C	U5L23: Speaking and Listening: Identify Ideas and Supporting Evidence	3
38	C	U5L23: Speaking and Listening: Identify Ideas and Supporting Evidence	1
39	A	U4L17: Speaking and Listening: Identify Ideas and Supporting Evidence	1

Item Number	Correct Answer	Unit, Lesson, Program Skill	Depth of Knowledge
		RESEARCH	
40	A, B, D	U4L19: Research and Media Literacy: Locate Information from Text Source	2
41	B	U5L24: Research and Media Literacy: Analyze Sources	2
42	B, E, F	U4L19: Research and Media Literacy: Interpret Information from Text Source	2
43	My favorite type...	U5L22: Research and Media Literacy: Interpret Information from Text Source	2
44	There is a net...	U5L22: Research and Media Literacy: Interpret Information from Text Source	2

Performance Task 3

Item Number	Correct Answer	Unit, Lesson, Program Skill	Depth of Knowledge
1	See rubric on p. T24.	U5L22: Research and Media Literacy: Interpret Information from Text Source	3
	Sample two-point response: Mateo Ramirez is the main person in "A Garden Grows." His ideas are the most important. He notices the vacant lot and thinks that the class should clean it up. Mateo writes to Madge Green to get her permission to clean the lot. Later, he thinks that the lot would be a good place for a community garden and gets permission to grow vegetables there. Gardeners donate their food to hungry people in the community. Mateo's ideas changed the community by using an old, empty lot to get food to the hungry.		
	Sample one-point response: Mateo Ramirez is the most important person in "A Garden Grows." He has good ideas. He thinks the vacant lot can be used for a community garden. Other people agree and plant vegetables there. The garden grows a lot of food for the community.		
2	See rubric on p. T24.	U5L24: Research and Media Literacy: Analyze Sources	4
	Sample two-point response: Money played an important role in both articles. Andrew Carnegie uses his money to build public libraries. The libraries Carnegie built with his money still provide communities with books and many other services. Mabel Dodge Luhan used money to give writers a place to live while they finished their works. Money allowed her to pay for the education of other people. The San Francisco Bay Bridge lights were designed by a man she helped. She used money to create a lasting change in the world.		
	Sample one-point response: Money played an important role because without it these people could not have done what they did. Mabel Luhan used her money to help people go to college.		
3	See answer below.	U5L24: Research and Media Literacy: Analyze Sources	3
	Success is best when it is shared with others: Source #1 and Source #3; Many hands make light work: Source #2; One individual can make a big difference: Source #1, Source #2, and Source #3; Those who have resources can help others: Source #1, Source #2, and Source #3; Something that is forgotten can become an important resource with the right care: Source #2		
Essay Response	See rubric on p. T26.	U5L25: Writing: Informative	4

Constructed-Response Rubrics

READING Rubric

Score of 2	• The response is logical and has an identifiable pattern/sequence. • The response provides adequate evidence of the student's ability to interpret information and/or make inferences and conclusions about the passage. • The response references clear evidence from the text that supports the student's response. • The response includes specific examples and/or details that relate to the text.
Score of 1	• The response is logical and connected to the prompt but may lack an identifiable pattern/sequence. • The response provides limited evidence of the student's ability to interpret information and/or make inferences and conclusions. • The response references little evidence from the text that supports the student's response. • The response includes some examples and/or details that relate to the text.
Score of 0	• The response provides no evidence of the student's ability to interpret information and/or make inferences and conclusions. • The response includes no relevant information, evidence, or examples from the text.

WRITING Rubric

Score of 2	• The response is logical, has an identifiable pattern/sequence, and is connected to the prompt. • The response provides and incorporates sufficient key points, reasons, details, and/or evidence to support the student's response. • The response includes elaboration and uses precise and specific words, language, and details.
Score of 1	• The response is mostly logical and connected to the prompt but may lack an identifiable pattern/sequence. • The response provides and incorporates limited key points, reasons, details, and/or evidence to support the student's response. • The response includes limited elaboration and uses general words, language, and details.
Score of 0	• The response has a weak or no connection to the prompt, may contradict the details/information in the prompt, or may restate provided details, introduce new or irrelevant details/information, or summarize the prompt. • The response gives no or an inappropriate opinion/introduction/central idea/conclusion and provides few or no key points, reasons, details, and/or evidence. • The response includes no elaboration and uses poor word choice.

Performance Task: Narrative Writing Rubric

Score	4	3	2	1	NS
Purpose/Organization	**The narrative is clear, focused, and well organized throughout.** • Contains an effective and complete plot • Develops a strong setting, narrator/characters • Includes a variety of transitions to connect ideas • Contains a logical sequence of events • Includes an effective introduction and conclusion	**The narrative's organization is adequately maintained, and the focus is generally clear.** • Plot is mostly effective/may contain small flaws • Develops setting, narrator/characters • Adequate use of transitions to connect ideas • Contains an adequate sequence of events • Includes adequate introduction and conclusion	**The narrative is somewhat organized and may be unclear in some parts. Plot may be inconsistent.** • Minimal development of setting, narrator/characters • Inconsistent use of transitions to connect ideas • Sequence of events is weak or unclear • Introduction and conclusion need improvement	**The narrative's focus and organization are not clear.** • Little or no plot • Little or no development of setting, narrator/characters • Contains few or inappropriate transitions and weak connections among ideas • Sequence of events is not organized • Introduction and/or conclusion may be missing	• Not intelligible • Not written in English • Not on topic • Contains text copied from source • Does not address the purpose for writing
Development/ Elaboration	**The narrative includes effective elaboration using details, dialogue, and description.** • Characters, setting, experiences, and events are well developed • Links to sources may enrich the narrative • Writer uses a variety of narrative techniques that strengthen the story or illustrate the experience • Contains effective sensory, concrete, and figurative language • Style is appropriate and effective	**The narrative includes adequate elaboration using details, dialogue, and description.** • Characters, setting, experiences, and events are adequately developed • Links to sources may contribute to the narrative • Writer uses a variety of narrative techniques that generally move the story forward and illustrate the experience • Contains adequate sensory, concrete, and figurative language • Style is mostly appropriate	**The narrative includes partial or ineffective elaboration using unclear or inconsistent details, dialogue, and description.** • Characters, setting, experiences, and events lack consistent development • Links to sources may be unsuccessful but do not detract from the narrative • Writer uses inconsistent or weak narrative techniques • Contains weak sensory, concrete, and figurative language • Style is inconsistent or inappropriate	**The narrative provides little or no elaboration using few or no details, dialogue, and description.** • Very little development of characters, setting, experiences, and events • Links to sources, if present, may interfere with the narrative • Writer's use of narrative techniques is minimal and may be incorrect • Little or no sensory, concrete, and figurative language • Little or no evidence of style	• Not intelligible • Not written in English • Not on topic • Contains text copied from source • Does not address the purpose for writing

Score	2	1	0	NS
Conventions	**The narrative demonstrates adequate command of conventions.** • Consistent use of correct sentence structures, punctuation, capitalization, grammar, and spelling	**The narrative demonstrates partial command of conventions.** • Limited use of correct sentence structures, punctuation, capitalization, grammar, and spelling	**The narrative demonstrates little or no command of conventions.** • Rare use of correct sentence structures, punctuation, capitalization, grammar, and spelling	• Not intelligible • Not written in English • Not on topic • Contains text copied from source

Performance Task: Informative/Explanatory Writing Rubric

Purpose/Organization

Score	4	3	2	1	NS
	The response is clear, focused, and well organized throughout.	**The response's organization is adequately maintained, and the focus is generally clear.**	**The response is somewhat focused but may be unclear in parts. Organization may be inconsistent.**	**The response's focus and organization are not clear.**	• Not intelligible
	• Main or central idea is clear, focused, and effective for task, audience, and purpose	• Main or central idea is clear, mostly focused, and mostly effective for task, audience, and purpose	• Main or central idea may be somewhat unclear, may lack focus, or may be ineffective for task, audience, and purpose	• Main or central idea may be confusing; response may be inappropriate for task, audience, and purpose	• Not written in English
	• Includes a variety of transitions to relate ideas	• Includes some variety of transitions to relate ideas	• Includes little variety of transitions to relate ideas	• Includes few or no transitions to relate ideas	• Not on topic
	• Contains a logical sequence of ideas with strong relationships between them	• Contains an adequate sequence of ideas with adequate relationships between them	• Sequence of ideas may be weak or unclear	• Sequence of ideas is unorganized; may include off-topic ideas	• Contains text copied from source
	• Includes an effective introduction and conclusion	• Includes an adequate introduction and conclusion	• Introduction and conclusion need improvement	• Introduction and/or conclusion may be missing	• Does not address the purpose for writing

Evidence/Elaboration

Score	4	3	2	1	NS
	The response presents strong support for the main and supporting ideas with effective use of evidence from sources, facts, and details, elaborating with specific and effective language.	**The response presents adequate support for the main and supporting ideas with evidence from sources, facts, and details, adequately elaborating with a mix of specific and general language.**	**The response presents inconsistent support for the main and supporting ideas with limited evidence from sources, facts, and details. Elaboration is inconsistent with simple language.**	**The response presents little support for the main and supporting ideas with little or no evidence from sources, facts, or details. Elaboration is inadequate or absent.**	• Not intelligible
	• Evidence from sources is integrated, is relevant, and supports key ideas	• Evidence from sources is integrated, is relevant, and adequately supports key ideas	• Evidence from sources may be poorly integrated or irrelevant, or only loosely supports key ideas	• Evidence from sources, if present, may be irrelevant with little support for key ideas	• Not written in English
	• Writer uses a variety of elaborative techniques	• Writer uses some elaborative techniques	• Writer uses few elaborative techniques	• Writer uses few or no elaborative techniques	• Not on topic
	• Vocabulary is clear and appropriate for task, audience, and purpose	• Vocabulary is mostly appropriate for task, audience, and purpose	• Vocabulary is somewhat inappropriate for task, audience, and purpose	• Vocabulary is inappropriate for task, audience, and purpose	• Contains text copied from source
	• Style is appropriate and effective	• Style is generally appropriate and effective	• Style is largely ineffective	• Style is weak or absent	• Does not address the purpose for writing

Conventions

Score	2	1	0	NS
	The response demonstrates adequate command of conventions.	**The response demonstrates partial command of conventions.**	**The response demonstrates little or no command of conventions.**	• Not intelligible
	• Consistent use of correct sentence structures, punctuation, capitalization, grammar, and spelling	• Limited use of correct sentence structures, punctuation, capitalization, grammar, and spelling	• Rare use of correct sentence structures; punctuation, capitalization, grammar, and spelling	• Not written in English
				• Not on topic
				• Contains text copied from source

Performance Task: Opinion Writing Rubric

Score	4	3	2	1	NS
Purpose/Organization	**The response is clear, focused, and well organized throughout.** • Opinion is clear, focused, and effective for task, audience, and purpose • Includes a variety of transitions to relate ideas • Contains a logical sequence of ideas with strong relationships between them • Includes an effective introduction and conclusion	**The response's organization is adequately maintained, and the focus is generally clear.** • Opinion is clear, mostly focused, and mostly effective for task, audience, and purpose • Includes some variety of transitions to relate ideas • Contains an adequate sequence of ideas with adequate relationships between them • Includes an adequate introduction and conclusion	**The response is somewhat focused but may be unclear in parts. Organization may be inconsistent.** • Opinion may be somewhat unclear, may lack focus, or may be ineffective for task, audience, and purpose • Includes little variety of transitions to relate ideas • Sequence of ideas may be weak or unclear • Introduction and conclusion need improvement	**The response's focus and organization are not clear.** • Opinion may be confusing; response may be inappropriate for task, audience, and purpose • Includes few or no transitions to relate ideas • Sequence of ideas is unorganized; may include off-topic ideas • Introduction and/or conclusion may be missing	• Not intelligible • Not written in English • Not on topic • Contains text copied from source • Does not address the purpose for writing
Evidence/ Elaboration	**The response presents strong support for the opinion with effective use of evidence from sources, facts, and details, elaborating with specific and effective language.** • Evidence from sources is integrated, is relevant, and supports key ideas • Writer uses a variety of elaborative techniques • Vocabulary is clear and appropriate for task, audience, and purpose • Style is appropriate and effective	**The response presents adequate support for the opinion with evidence from sources, facts, and details, adequately elaborating with a mix of specific and general language.** • Evidence from sources is integrated, is relevant, and adequately supports key ideas • Writer uses some elaborative techniques • Vocabulary is mostly appropriate for task, audience, and purpose • Style is generally appropriate and effective	**The response presents inconsistent support for the opinion with limited evidence from sources, facts, and details. Elaboration is inconsistent with simple language.** • Evidence from sources may be poorly integrated or irrelevant, or only loosely supports key ideas • Writer uses few elaborative techniques • Vocabulary is somewhat inappropriate for task, audience, and purpose • Style is largely ineffective	**The response presents little support for the opinion with little or no evidence from sources, facts, or details. Elaboration is inadequate or absent.** • Evidence from sources, if present, may be irrelevant with little support for key ideas • Writer uses few or no elaborative techniques • Vocabulary is inappropriate for task, audience, and purpose • Style is weak or absent	• Not intelligible • Not written in English • Not on topic • Contains text copied from source • Does not address the purpose for writing

Score	2	1	0	NS
Conventions	**The response demonstrates adequate command of conventions.** • Consistent use of correct sentence structures, punctuation, capitalization, grammar, and spelling	**The response demonstrates partial command of conventions.** • Limited use of correct sentence structures, punctuation, capitalization, grammar, and spelling	**The response demonstrates little or no command of conventions.** • Rare use of correct sentence structures, punctuation, capitalization, grammar, and spelling	• Not intelligible • Not written in English • Not on topic • Contains text copied from source

Test Record Form

Student Name _____

Assessment 1   Date _____

Date Administered _____		Possible Score	Acceptable Score	Student Score
Reading (Items 1–20)*	Selected-Response	18	16	
	Constructed-Response	4		
Writing (Items 21–30)*	Selected-Response	9	8	
	Constructed-Response	2		
Listening (Items 31–39)		9	7	
Research (Items 40–44)		5	4	
	Total	47	35	
	FINAL SCORE = Total Student Score x 2.12 = _____			

Performance Task 1   Date _____

Date Administered _____		Possible Score	Acceptable Score	Student Score
Part 1 (Items 1–3)*	Selected-Response	1	4	
	Constructed-Response	4		
Part 2 (Essay Response)		10	7	
	Total	15	11	
	Total Student Score x 6.67 = _____			

Assessment 2   Date _____

Date Administered _____		Possible Score	Acceptable Score	Student Score
Reading (Items 1–20)*	Selected-Response	18	16	
	Constructed-Response	4		
Writing (Items 21–30)*	Selected-Response	9	8	
	Constructed-Response	2		
Listening (Items 31–39)		9	7	
Research (Items 40–44)		5	4	
	Total	47	35	
	FINAL SCORE = Total Student Score x 2.12 = _____			

Performance Task 2   Date _____

Date Administered _____		Possible Score	Acceptable Score	Student Score
Part 1 (Items 1–3)*	Selected-Response	1	4	
	Constructed-Response	4		
Part 2 (Essay Response)		10	7	
	Total	15	11	
	Total Student Score x 6.67 = _____			

Assessment 3   Date _____

Date Administered _____		Possible Score	Acceptable Score	Student Score
Reading (Items 1–20)*	Selected-Response	18	16	
	Constructed-Response	4		
Writing (Items 21–30)*	Selected-Response	9	8	
	Constructed-Response	2		
Listening (Items 31–39)		9	7	
Research (Items 40–44)		5	4	
	Total	47	35	
	FINAL SCORE = Total Student Score x 2.12 = _____			

Performance Task 3   Date _____

Date Administered _____		Possible Score	Acceptable Score	Student Score
Part 1 (Items 1–3)*	Selected-Response	1	4	
	Constructed-Response	4		
Part 2 (Essay Response)		10	7	
	Total	15	11	
	Total Student Score x 6.67 = _____			

*This section includes constructed-response items worth up to two points each. Please note when scoring.

Assessment 1
Reading

Read the passage. Then answer the questions.

The Mysterious Tree

I had always thought that Fernwood, the town where I live, was an ordinary town. The homes were ordinary, the people were ordinary, and even our pets were ordinary. A sign in front of the courthouse read: Welcome to Fernwood! An Ordinary, Peaceful Town.

Then one day, I was out with my friends Phillipe and Rosa. We were walking in the town square, going back to my place after school like we did every day. As we approached the courthouse, Rosa looked up and suddenly stopped in her tracks. "What's coming out of the courthouse roof?" she asked. She held up her hand to shield her eyes. The sun was shining into our faces, so it was hard to see. "Whatever it is, it certainly isn't ordinary!"

"Hey," said Phillipe, squinting. "I think it's a little green leaf."

"I see two leaves," I said as I looked up.

"It looks like a little tree growing up there!" said Rosa, straining her eyes against the sun. She looked beyond the old-fashioned clock toward the gleaming white spire sticking out above it.

"If we tell anyone about it, they might pressure Mayor Kaplan to get rid of it," said Phillipe. "Let's give that little tree a chance to grow."

Before we knew it, school was over; summer had arrived, and to our surprise, our days were filled with some not-so-ordinary events. Phillipe's cat Roco, who had been lost since last year, mysteriously returned home. Phillipe discovered him meowing at his back door early one morning. They never figured out where he had been. Then Rosa found $20 in her library book. She returned the money to the library and when no one claimed it, it became hers. My not-so-ordinary event was a big surprise to both my softball team and me. I hit my first home run ever during a game against our biggest rival. We were down by three runs and did not think we could come back to win. My home run happened to be a grand slam that won the game.

Name _____ Date _____

Whenever we were downtown near the courthouse that summer, we looked up at its roof and couldn't help but marvel at that curious little tree still perched there, high above the town. Rosa, Phillipe, and I wondered if we were the only ones who noticed it.

When fall came, the town council decided to spruce up the clock tower by giving it a new coat of paint. Of course, when the painters scaled the courthouse clock tower, they discovered the little tree. My friends and I decided to go to the next town meeting. We were worried that the adults might only be able to see this tree one way: as an annoyance. As for us, we imagined that the tree might be linked to all the astonishing things that had happened to us over the summer. We thought it would be a good idea to return the favor and protect this little tree.

The night of the town meeting, Phillipe spoke. "No one has ever heard of a tree growing out of a roof. That makes this tree unique. Please don't cut it down. It brought my friends and me luck all summer." The vote was unanimous that the tree could stay where it was. Today the town sign reads: Welcome to Fernwood! Home of the Famous Courthouse Tree.

---

1 Read the sentences from the passage.

> When fall came, the town council decided to spruce up the clock tower by giving it a new coat of paint. Of course, when the painters <u>scaled</u> the courthouse clock tower, they discovered the little tree.

What does <u>scaled</u> **most likely** mean?

Ⓐ scraped

Ⓑ climbed

Ⓒ weighed

Ⓓ investigated

Name _____   Date _____

2 Read the sentences from the passage.

> As we approached the courthouse, Rosa looked up and suddenly stopped in her tracks. "What's coming out of the courthouse roof?" she asked. She held up her hand to shield her eyes. The sun was shining into our faces, so it was hard to see.

What is the **most likely** reason the narrator thought the sun shining was important?

- Ⓐ It gave a clue about what season it was.
- Ⓑ It meant the tree would get enough light.
- Ⓒ It showed that some people might not see the tree.
- Ⓓ It showed that Rosa really wanted to see the top of the spire even though it was hard.

3 Underline **three** sentences from the passage that explain why Rosa, Phillipe, and the narrator decide to attend the town meeting.

> When fall came, the town council decided to spruce up the clock tower by giving it a new coat of paint. Of course, when the painters scaled the courthouse clock tower, they discovered the little tree. My friends and I decided to go to the next town meeting. We were worried that the adults might only be able to see this tree one way: as an annoyance. As for us, we imagined that the tree might be linked to all the astonishing things that had happened to us over the summer. We thought it would be a good idea to return the favor and protect this little tree.

4 Which idea **best** describes the theme of the story?

Ⓐ Trees can bring good luck to people.

Ⓑ You can get others to see your side of things.

Ⓒ Unusual things can happen in ordinary places.

Ⓓ Friends should work together to make things happen.

5 Which words **best** describe the characters in this passage? Choose **two**.

Ⓐ lonely

Ⓑ caring

Ⓒ mean

Ⓓ strong

Ⓔ tough

Ⓕ watchful

Assessment 1
4
Grade 4

Name _____   Date _____

Read the passage. Then answer the questions.

Growing a Patch of the Prairie

Kimberly was on her way to the library when she saw her neighbor, Mrs. Lin, standing in her yard. Mrs. Lin was writing "For Sale" on a piece of cardboard. On the sidewalk were a lawn mower, two sprinklers, and four garden hoses. Kimberly thought it was odd that Mrs. Lin would want to sell all her garden tools.

"What are you doing, having a yard sale?" Kimberly asked Mrs. Lin.

"Yes, I'm selling my lawn and everything I need to care for it," said Mrs. Lin, happy with her misdirection.

"How can you sell your lawn?" Kimberly asked. She was puzzled.

"Well, I'm not selling the lawn," said Mrs. Lin. "I'm just getting a new kind of grass to plant here."

Mrs. Lin's lawn was so pretty that marching bands from around the state came to practice on it. There was a good reason for that. Mrs. Lin was always working in her yard. The grass was a beautiful shade of green. It did not have any bare spots or weeds.

"Why would you ever want to change your perfect lawn into something else?" Kimberly asked.

"I know it's perfect, but that's because I work on it and water it so much. I've decided that's perfectly wrong for the kind of area where we live. In the summer, we have periods when there is no rain and the ground is as dry as a bone. I don't want to waste water by using it on my lawn. That's why I asked the man at the garden shop to bring me buffalo grass to plant here instead."

Kimberly thought about the kind of grass that buffaloes would eat. She imagined a little piece of the Great Plains in Mrs. Lin's yard. She had been learning about the plants of the Great Plains in school. "Are you planting a prairie in your yard?" she asked.

"Yes, I guess you could say that," Mrs. Lin said with a smile. "Buffalo grass is the same grass that settlers used to build sod houses on the prairies. They used it because there was a lot of it all around. You can grow it in this climate without much water. If it only rains every now and then, the lawn will be just fine."

"Now I understand why you're selling the sprinklers and hoses. You will have to cut the buffalo grass, so won't you still need your lawn mower?" Kimberly asked.

Mrs. Lin smiled like a child letting out a big secret. "Since buffalo grass grows only eight inches tall, I'll only have to mow it a couple of times a year. I'm going to get a mower that I can push by myself. Without that loud engine running, I'll be able to hear the birds while I cut the grass. Plus, I won't be using gas or electricity to mow. It will be good exercise."

"But if you're not taking care of your grass, when will I see you?" Kimberly asked with a frown. Kimberly and Mrs. Lin usually talked during gardening time. Kimberly did not want to miss out on her time with Mrs. Lin.

Mrs. Lin seemed pleased by Kimberly's question. She pointed to her porch and said, "Those two chairs are for us to sit in while we look at the buffalo grass. We can admire the yard as we drink lemonade and chat. I'll not only have more time to spend with you, but I'll be helping the environment too."

---

6 Mrs. Lin tells Kimberly that she will save water by planting buffalo grass. In what other way will the new grass help the environment?

Ⓐ Mrs. Lin will spend less money.

Ⓑ Mrs. Lin will get more exercise.

Ⓒ Mrs. Lin will not have to mow as often.

Ⓓ Mrs. Lin will not need gas or electricity to mow.

7 Why does Kimberly think it is odd that Mrs. Lin would sell her garden tools?

    Ⓐ Mrs. Lin does a lot of gardening.

    Ⓑ Mrs. Lin doesn't need the money.

    Ⓒ Mrs. Lin's garden tools are very old.

    Ⓓ Mrs. Lin won't be outside to talk anymore.

8 This question has two parts. First, answer part A. Then, answer part B.

Part A

Read the sentences from the passage.

> "What are you doing, having a yard sale?" Kimberly asked Mrs. Lin.

> "Yes, I'm selling my lawn and everything I need to care for it," said Mrs. Lin, happy with her misdirection.

What was Mrs. Lin's misdirection?

    Ⓐ She was trying to tell Kimberly to buy her lawn.

    Ⓑ She wanted Kimberly to believe she was moving.

    Ⓒ She wanted Kimberly to understand she was getting a new lawn.

    Ⓓ She knew that she wasn't having the kind of yard sale Kimberly meant.

Part B

Read the sentences from the passage.

> "How can you sell your lawn?" Kimberly asked. She was puzzled.

Why was Kimberly puzzled? Choose the **most likely** reason.

    Ⓐ She didn't understand that Mrs. Lin meant only the lawn and not the yard.

    Ⓑ She thought Mrs. Lin was moving.

    Ⓒ Mrs. Lin was happy, but selling a lawn is a sad thing.

    Ⓓ Kimberly didn't want to miss out on her time with Mrs. Lin.

Name _____ Date _____

9 Which sentence from the passage includes an example of hyperbole?

Ⓐ "Mrs. Lin's lawn was so pretty that marching bands from around the state came to practice on it."

Ⓑ "She imagined a little piece of the Great Plains in Mrs. Lin's yard."

Ⓒ "Mrs. Lin smiled like a child letting out a big secret."

Ⓓ "Kimberly didn't want to miss out on her time with Mrs. Lin."

10 Compare the narration of "The Mysterious Tree" and "Growing a Patch of the Prairie." Whose point of view is represented in each passage, and how does this help or not help the reader understand each story? Be sure to include whether each passage is told in the first-person or third-person perspective. Include examples from each passage to support your answer.

_____

_____

_____

_____

_____

Name _____ Date _____

Read the passage. Then answer the questions.

When Disaster Strikes

Hurricane Katrina slammed into New Orleans, Louisiana, in 2005. The devastation it caused was heartbreaking. Whole neighborhoods were reduced to rubble. Many people lost their lives, and others were trapped by rising floods. The floods rose after the levees broke days after the storm. Levees are built to hold back water in places where the land is below the water's level.

It is hard to picture such destruction. The city still has not fully recovered. Soon after Katrina hit, Steve Pendergrass and his dog Marc were called in. They were one of dozens of dog rescue teams whose job was to search for survivors. Each morning they were up at 5:30 to begin searching. Marc spent long hours crawling over the rubble. He ended the day with sore muscles and bruises. But the heroic dog never gave up. Steve needs Marc's skills because dogs can crawl into spaces where a man can't fit. Dogs also have better senses of hearing and smell than humans.

Marc's hard work paid off one day when he helped rescue a 74-year-old man. National Guard members had to break into the house. The man was unconscious and near death. With him was a puppy, which was also rescued.

Recently, disaster rescue dogs like Marc have become more important. Some of the dogs are certified by the Federal Emergency Management Agency or FEMA. FEMA is the U.S. government agency that helps in disasters around the country. The FEMA certificate means the dogs have completed training and can work in disaster situations. These rescue dogs are sometimes called "urban search and rescue dogs." They are given this name because they often work in cities affected by disasters.

Disaster rescue dogs search in dangerous conditions. They must be fit enough to work long hours. They also must be able to work independently away from their handlers. They must be careful not to fall or get caught in anything. Dogs frequently work without a collar or a harness, which could get caught on wreckage. A disaster rescue dog cannot be too large. Too much weight might cause rubble to collapse. Very small dogs are not suited to the work, either. They have trouble making their way across gaps.

During a real emergency, no one knows whether any people will be found. It's important for a rescue dog to feel a sense of accomplishment. Many rescue dogs get a reward after finishing a job. This reward helps keep the dog happy and hardworking. For example, the dog might get to play fetch or another game after it rescues someone. In that way, working dogs are not very different from dogs who don't work. If a dog finishes searching and doesn't discover anyone, a handler may ask a person to hide. Then the dog is sent to find the pretend "victim" and receives its usual reward.

Training a search and rescue dog is a big job. It can take years of hard work. Then the dog and its handler must spend hours each week practicing. They spend a lot of time together and must have a close relationship. Most rescue dog handlers are volunteers who spend their own money and time. The dogs they train are also their pets.

Some of the best rescue dogs have been saved from animal shelters. A pet dog with a lot of curiosity and extra energy can become destructive. It needs a lot of exercise. A dog may also become bored if it doesn't have a job. But that same dog may shine when someone challenges it with the important job of search and rescue.

Name _____ Date _____

11 Read the paragraph from the passage.

Marc's hard work paid off one day when he helped rescue a 74-year-old man. National Guard members had to break into the house. The man was unconscious and near death. With him was a puppy, which was also rescued.

What are the **most likely** reasons the author mentions that Marc helped rescue a 74-year-old man? Choose **two**.

Ⓐ to show that Marc should get paid

Ⓑ to show that Marc needs more training

Ⓒ to show that Marc was helpful after the hurricane

Ⓓ to show that Marc could not save the man himself

Ⓔ to show that training rescue dogs like Marc is important

Ⓕ to show that Marc heard the puppy so he was able to find the man

12 This question has two parts. First, answer part A. Then, answer part B.

Part A

Based on the map in the passage, what is the **most likely** reason New Orleans suffered such damage after Hurricane Katrina?

Ⓐ People were not prepared.

Ⓑ The city is surrounded by water.

Ⓒ The buildings were not strong enough.

Ⓓ People did not think the storm would be that strong.

Part B

Which sentence from the passage **best** supports the answer to part A?

Ⓐ "Whole neighborhoods were reduced to rubble."

Ⓑ "Many people lost their lives, and others were trapped by rising floods."

Ⓒ "It is hard to picture such destruction."

Ⓓ "The city still has not fully recovered."

13 Read the sentences from the passage.

> Each morning they were up at 5:30 to begin searching. Marc spent long hours crawling over the <u>rubble</u>. He ended the day with sore muscles and bruises.

Which word is the **best** choice to replace the word <u>rubble</u>?

- Ⓐ junk
- Ⓑ houses
- Ⓒ mountain
- Ⓓ wreckage

14 Read the paragraph from the passage. Underline **one** sentence that gives an example of why rescue dogs cannot be too large.

> Disaster rescue dogs search in dangerous conditions. They must be fit enough to work long hours. They also must be able to work independently away from their handlers. They must be careful not to fall or get caught in anything. Dogs frequently work without a collar or a harness, which could get caught on wreckage. A disaster rescue dog cannot be too large. Too much weight might cause rubble to collapse. Very small dogs are not suited to the work, either. They have trouble making their way across gaps.

15 Read the sentences from the passage.

> If a dog finishes searching and doesn't <u>discover</u> anyone, a handler may ask a person to hide. Then the dog is sent to find the pretend "victim" and receives its usual reward.

What is the **best** definition for <u>discover</u> as it is used in the passage?

- Ⓐ find
- Ⓑ hide
- Ⓒ work
- Ⓓ answer

Name _____   Date _____

Read the passage. Then answer the questions.

Instinct and Intelligence

Human intelligence is the ability to learn and to understand new situations. This intelligence comes in many different forms. Think about people you know. Some of them are very skilled at solving problems using logic. Others are better at using information on hand. Humans have the ability to solve problems, learn new things, and make decisions. This is because they have good memories and can use language well.

It is important to distinguish between intelligence and instinct. An instinct is a living being's natural understanding of how to act or how to do something. For instance, a spider's instincts tell it how to spin a web. The spider did not have to learn how to do this. Many animals, including humans, use their instincts to respond to their environment. For example, when it gets dark outside, your instinct tells you that you are tired. You don't have to learn how to sleep. You were born able to do so. You are displaying an instinct. However, when you learn how to do something, you are displaying intelligence. You were not born knowing how to read this passage. You learned. Although scientists have tried to teach some monkeys, so far they remain illiterate. Some baboons, however, can tell the difference between fake words and real ones. The difference between humans and baboons is that baboons cannot tell what the words mean.

Animals also possess intelligence. Scientists have studied the abilities of different species to perform mental tasks. These require thinking and reasoning. Scientists consider chimpanzees to be among the most intelligent animal species. Dolphins, birds, and dogs are considered to be very intelligent, too.

Name _____ Date _____

The ability to solve problems is one of the best signs of intelligence. The chimpanzee, or chimp, is also an excellent problem solver. In order to test chimps' intelligence, scientists give them mental tasks to perform. Scientists might hang a treat where a chimp cannot reach it. The scientists then wait for the chimp to solve the problem. The chimp might stack boxes or logs and then stand on them to reach the treat. It might make or find a pointed stick and use that to reach the treat. In the wild, chimpanzees use grass, sticks, and leaves as tools. The tools help them gather food and hunt prey. A chimp will put a stick into an ant hole and use it to gather ants to eat. Chimps also use rocks and wood as hammers to crack the hard shells of nuts. Smart stuff! The ability to use tools is a characteristic, or trait, that helps chimps survive.

Other animals also use tools. Scientists have discovered that alligators use small sticks to attract birds. The birds are looking for building materials for their nests. An unsuspecting bird may try to grab the stick and become an alligator snack. Scientists do not know enough about alligators to know how intelligent they may be.

They are learning, however, how intelligent elephants are. Experiments have shown that elephants can use tools to get food that is out of reach. They also remember the strategy the next time they need it.

Although scientists agree that baboons learn easily, they don't agree about how intelligent they are. Are baboons smart? Or are they just very good at copying what they see? Some scientists believe that primates can perform tasks without really learning anything. In fact, the English language has several expressions that mimic this belief. One of them is "monkey see, monkey do."

16 Read the sentences. Underline the word that means <u>cannot read</u>.

You were not born knowing how to read this passage. You learned. Although scientists have tried to teach some monkeys, so far they remain illiterate. Some baboons, however, can tell the difference between fake words and real ones. The difference between humans and baboons is that baboons cannot tell what the words mean.

17 This question has two parts. First, answer part A. Then, answer part B.

Part A

Read the sentences from the passage.

Some scientists believe that primates can perform tasks without really learning anything. In fact, the English language has several expressions that <u>mimic</u> this belief. One of them is "<u>monkey see, monkey do</u>."

What is the **best** explanation for the idiom "<u>monkey see, monkey do</u>"?

Ⓐ Monkeys learn by copying what they see others do.

Ⓑ Monkeys don't do anything unless they see it done first.

Ⓒ Monkeys are good actors because they can copy anyone.

Ⓓ Monkeys copy things, but they may not be learning from them.

Part B

What is the **most likely** reason the author chose to use the word <u>mimic</u> in the sentence above?

Ⓐ Because "mimic" can also mean "copy" and it shows what the scientists think.

Ⓑ Because "mimic" can also mean "play" and it shows what the scientists think.

Ⓒ Because "mimic" can also mean "learn" and it shows what the scientists think.

Ⓓ Because "mimic" can also mean "pretend" and it shows what the scientists think.

18 One way scientists decide whether an animal is intelligent is if it understands cause and effect. Which experiment would give scientists the **most** information to help with that decision?

Ⓐ Throw a stick to see if a dog chases it.

Ⓑ Let a bird out of a cage to see if it flies away.

Ⓒ Turn off the lights to see if an animal goes to sleep.

Ⓓ Give an elephant a stool to see if it stands on it to reach food.

19 If you wanted to learn up-to-date information about animal intelligence and instinct, which **two** resources would be the **best** places to look?

Ⓐ a pet store website

Ⓑ an online encyclopedia

Ⓒ a book published in 1999

Ⓓ a magazine for dog lovers

Ⓔ a fictional passage about apes

Ⓕ a website about animal research

20 Using information and examples from both passages, explain whether you think Marc is using intelligence or instinct in his job as a rescue dog.

_____

_____

_____

_____

_____

Writing

Read and answer each question.

21 Matt is writing about a school project. Read the sentences from his story.

> We will paint a mural about pioneer days. We will paint a mountain <u>peak</u> in the distance. In the front we will show a barn with a weather <u>vain.</u> Behind the barn there will be a <u>herd</u> of cows. Our painting will be quite a <u>feat.</u>

What change should be made to an underlined word to correct a spelling error?

Ⓐ Change "peak" to "peek"

Ⓑ Change "vain" to "vane"

Ⓒ Change "herd" to "heard"

Ⓓ Change "feat" to "feet"

22 Which sentence has an error in grammar usage?

Ⓐ He "said I can see you just pretend to believe me."

Ⓑ He said that I was just pretending to believe him.

Ⓒ He said, "I can see you just pretend to believe me."

Ⓓ He said that I could not even pretend to believe him.

23 Tim is writing a story about an event in his community. Read his description. Underline **two** parts of the paragraph that are sentence fragments.

> Our school parade happens just before school starts every year. The reason for the parade is to start a fresh school year. The mayor in her blue car. The fire chief waves from a fire truck. The police chief walks in front of the police band. A tall man with gray hair, a tiny bike. Volunteer clowns do lots of tricks. Some clowns pretend to be teachers. One clown spins a giant globe. The teacher clowns remind parents and kids how to prepare for school. Everyone is eager to witness the fun and magic of our parade.

Name _____   Date _____

24 Choose the sentence that is punctuated correctly.

Ⓐ Believe me, I got quite a fright tonight?

Ⓑ Where can we find a good, cheap restaurant!

Ⓒ Remind me to tell you a story about my grandfather.

Ⓓ I have finished my homework and it is time for supper?

25 Janet is writing a story about her ancestors. This is her first draft. She wants to revise the draft to eliminate errors and make the writing better. Read the beginning of Janet's story. Underline the **two** words that have spelling errors.

> The first time Joan saw Nate Watson, he was trying to race a train. Joan was riding on the train. Nate was driving a wagon that was pulled with much work by a horse. Joan waved at Nate as the train steemed past him and he disappeared from sight. The train rounded a long bend. It slowed down as it came near a town. It rolled to a stop at a small station. Looking up the street, Joan saw a man trying to control a horse. The beast was rearing from fright and about to tip the wagon into the dich. It was the young man she had seen from the train!

26 Reread this sentence from Janet's story.

> Nate was driving a wagon that was <u>pulled with much work</u> by a horse.

She wants to replace the <u>underlined</u> words to make her meaning clearer. Which word would be a **better** choice?

Ⓐ moved

Ⓑ pushed

Ⓒ dragged

Ⓓ transported

Name _____ Date _____

27 Janet decides that her story needs even more details. She adds a sentence and changes another sentence so that it has more concrete details. The underlined sentences show Janet's changes.

> The train rounded a long bend. It slowed down as it came near a town. <u>The whistle blew a long, loud blast. The train roared to a stop at a small station.</u> Looking up the street, Joan saw a man trying to control a horse.

What are **two** reasons that adding these concrete details made the story better?

Ⓐ The details explain how the train worked.

Ⓑ The details describe what the train sounded like.

Ⓒ The details make Joan's train journey seem more important.

Ⓓ The details help explain why Nate's horse was rearing from fright.

Ⓔ The details help explain why Joan felt the way she did about Nate.

28 Here is the next section of Janet's story. Read the paragraphs.

> "Wind River!" called the conductor. "This stop is Wind River!"
>
> Joan jumped up with delight and pulled her bags down from the shelf overhead. Before long she was on the platform watching the train speed away. She was here at last. This was her first job as a teacher. Maybe the long grind of her studies for the past three years would now pay off. Maybe this was her big chance to build a career for herself at the Wind River School, which was the only school in the district. Joan was eager to start work, but she was afraid, too.

The last sentence of the passage is not the best ending. Which sentence should move to the end of the passage?

Ⓐ This was her first job as a teacher.

Ⓑ "Wind River!" called the conductor. "This stop is Wind River!"

Ⓒ Before long she was on the platform watching the train speed away.

Ⓓ Maybe the long grind of her studies for the past three years would now pay off.

Name _____ Date _____

29 Next Janet writes a section about how Joan met Nate. Read the new section.

> Joan turned around and saw the young man with the farm cart. He took his hat off and bowed to her. "My name is Nate Watson," he said.
>
> Joan watched the young man load her bags onto the cart. Then he helped her make the steep climb up into the front seat. He took the reins and called to his horse. Soon they were heading down the road toward the school where Joan would work. She felt as if her life were a dream.

Which sentence would make the **best** beginning for this section of the story?

  Ⓐ   Joan gave a sigh because she was tired from her long ride.

  Ⓑ   The platform seemed remote, and Joan wondered what to do.

  Ⓒ   Joan watched the train go farther and farther away until it was only a distant speck.

  Ⓓ   "Excuse me," said a man's voice. "But are you Miss Joan Munson, the new teacher?"

30 Read the last paragraph again. Rewrite it to be more descriptive. Be sure to include details and sensory words.

> Joan watched the young man load her bags onto the cart. Then he helped her make the steep climb up into the front seat. He took the reins and called to his horse. Soon they were heading down the road toward the school where Joan would work. She felt as if her life were a dream.

_____

_____

_____

_____

Name _____ Date _____

Listening

Listen to the presentation. Then answer the questions.

History and Harlem

Name _____   Date _____

31 Which phrase expresses the main idea of the presentation?

Ⓐ New York City

Ⓑ the Harlem Renaissance

Ⓒ writers, artists, and musicians

Ⓓ the first truly American music

32 Which detail from the presentation **best** supports the conclusion that Harlem played an important role in American history?

Ⓐ Harlem is part of New York City.

Ⓑ The Harlem Renaissance took place during the 1920s and 1930s.

Ⓒ Tourists visit places in Harlem where famous people once lived.

Ⓓ People heard jazz at the Savoy Ballroom, the Cotton Club, and the Apollo Theater.

33 Select **two** conclusions that are supported by the presentation.

Ⓐ An important landmark in New York City is in Harlem.

Ⓑ Money was scarcer in the 1920s and 1930s than it is today.

Ⓒ Harlem is especially important to African American history.

Ⓓ In Harlem, writers, artists, dancers, and musicians were neighbors.

Ⓔ Jazz music was the most important art form during the Harlem Renaissance.

Name _____ Date _____

Listen to the presentation. Then answer the questions.

Toe Shoes and Tutus

Name _____ Date _____

34 Which detail from the presentation **best** supports the conclusion that ballet has been an art form for at least 500 years?

Ⓐ Ballet began in Italy in the 1400s.

Ⓑ Catherine de Medici brought it to France in the mid-1500s.

Ⓒ Russia began to lead the ballet world at the end of the 1800s.

Ⓓ Russian dance companies toured the globe in the early 1900s.

35 This question has two parts. First, answer part A. Then, answer part B.

Part A

What is the **most likely** purpose of the presentation?

Ⓐ to explain why audiences like ballet

Ⓑ to describe ballet in history and today

Ⓒ to compare the ballet styles of France and Russia

Ⓓ to explain why ballet dancers stand on their toes and wear tutus

Part B

Which detail from the presentation **best** supports your answer in part A?

Ⓐ Catherine de Medici married King Henry II of France.

Ⓑ A ballet might tell a story or evoke an idea or an emotion.

Ⓒ The dancers in the first picture were standing on their toes.

Ⓓ Even today, all the ballet positions, steps, and jumps have French names.

36 Which detail from the presentation **best** supports the conclusion that more people than ever before dance ballet today?

Ⓐ Ballets started appearing in theaters.

Ⓑ Today, many countries have ballet companies and ballet schools.

Ⓒ It takes years to train to do all the steps to perfection and in time with the music and the other dancers.

Ⓓ A ballet might tell a story or evoke an idea or emotion.

Name _____ Date _____

Listen to the presentation. Then answer the questions.

Protecting Valuable Resources

37 Select **two** conclusions that are supported by the presentation.

Ⓐ Trees provide raw materials for the lumber industry.

Ⓑ New products made from trees appear on the market all the time.

Ⓒ The lumber industry is one of the nation's biggest sources of jobs.

Ⓓ Today we are destroying trees faster than we can save or replant them.

Ⓔ Trees are important natural resources that we must conserve, protect, and preserve.

38 What is the **main** purpose of the presentation?

Ⓐ to teach people about the value of trees

Ⓑ to point out how many jobs depend on trees

Ⓒ to persuade people to protect trees and forests

Ⓓ to describe why trees make us healthy and happy

Name _____ Date _____

39 This question has two parts. First, answer part A. Then, answer part B.

Part A

Read this sentence from the presentation.

> Trees are valuable resources. We must be careful not to use too many of them.

What would happen if there were not enough trees? Select the **best** conclusion from the details in the presentation.

Ⓐ Many workers in the lumber industry would lose their jobs.

Ⓑ The prices of wood, paper, cloth, and other products would fall.

Ⓒ The environment would be able to provide food and shelter for animals.

Ⓓ People would stop working together to plant new trees and protect forests.

Part B

Which detail from the presentation **best** supports your answer in part A?

Ⓐ But trees are valuable for much more than their products.

Ⓑ They are sources of food and shelter for animals, and they help reduce water pollution.

Ⓒ Machines turn the timber into boards, chips, and pulp.

Ⓓ For each of these jobs, other workers have to make and sell supplies and equipment.

Name _____ Date _____

Research

Read and answer each question.

40 A student is writing a report about the history of Thanksgiving in America. The student found several sources. Which sources would **most likely** have information for the report? Choose **two** sources.

Ⓐ *Reasons to Be Thankful*

A book that lists 100 reasons to be thankful on Thanksgiving

Ⓑ *The First Thanksgiving*

A book about the Pilgrims' first Thanksgiving in the New World in 1621

Ⓒ *Holidays Around the World*

A book about how different countries celebrate their own Thanksgivings

Ⓓ "How to Cook a Turkey"

An article in a cooking magazine about how to cook a turkey for Thanksgiving

Ⓔ www.thanksgivingdecorating.org

A website with instructions about how to make holiday decorations for Thanksgiving

Ⓕ www.thanksgivinginamerica.com

A website that describes how Thanksgiving in America has changed throughout the years

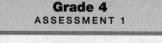

Name _____ Date _____

41 A student is writing a report about volunteering. She wrote the following opinion: Volunteering makes people happy. She found a source. Read the source and underline the **two** sentences that best support the opinion.

The Benefits of Volunteering

Many people volunteer because they want to help others. They say they want to give back to their communities. They also want to help people in need. But volunteering is good for your health, too.

Scientists have discovered that people who volunteer are less depressed than other people. Volunteering makes people feel better about themselves. Some people may be surprised by these facts. The truth is that when you help others, you are also helping yourself.

Name _____ Date _____

42 A student is writing a report about the types of work George Washington did before he became president. She found a timeline. Read the timeline.

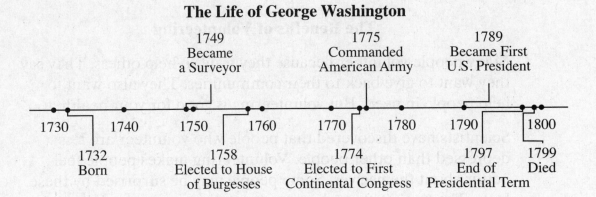

The Life of George Washington

1749
Became
a Surveyor

1775
Commanded
American Army

1789
Became First
U.S. President

1730   1740   1750   1760   1770   1780   1790   1800

1732
Born

1758
Elected to House
of Burgesses

1774
Elected to First
Continental Congress

1797
End of
Presidential Term

1799
Died

The student found a second source. Read the second source.

George Washington is known as the first president of the United States. However, before he became president, he had a very interesting life. Washington was born in Virginia in 1732. His father died when George was a young boy. Washington went to work when he was a teenager. He became a surveyor, which is a person who takes measurements of land. He was very good at this job. He then joined the Virginia militia and fought in the French and Indian War.

Which detail from the second source supports the information in the timeline?

Ⓐ "However, before he became president, he had a very interesting life."

Ⓑ "His father died when George was a young boy."

Ⓒ "He became a surveyor, which is a person who takes measurements of land."

Ⓓ "He then joined the Virginia militia and fought in the French and Indian War."

43 A student is writing a research report about honeybees. Read the excerpt from one of the sources he found.

Honeybees: An Important Resource by Luisa Reyes

Did you know that honeybees are disappearing? The population of honeybees in the United States has dropped a lot in the past 10 years. We must stop this from happening. Honeybees are an important part of our lives.

Honeybees do much more than produce honey. They pollinate flowers and most of the fruits and vegetables we eat. Without honeybees, these plants would not grow. It is hard to imagine a world without fruits and vegetables. Without honeybees, this is exactly what would happen.

The source states that honeybees are an important part of our lives. Choose **two** reasons the author gives to support this point.

Ⓐ Honeybees live in colonies.

Ⓑ Honeybees help plants grow.

Ⓒ Honeybees prefer warm climates.

Ⓓ The United States has already lost many of its honeybees.

Ⓔ Honeybees prefer to pollinate some flowers more than others.

Ⓕ By pollinating plants, honeybees make it possible for us to have food to eat.

44 A student is writing a report about how photographers can change people's lives. Read the paragraphs from a source about life in the Mississippi Delta. Underline a sentence from the paragraphs that has information the student should use in the report.

The lives of farm workers and others in the Delta area were not always easy. People often worked long hours for only a little pay. Writers told stories about the many misfortunes. Photographers often took pictures of the people.

Rogerline Johnson was different. He wanted to show the whole story of the people of his area. He knew that the Delta people could also be happy and successful. He took pictures of people enjoying themselves. He took pictures of people playing music or riding in a car. He wanted to show that the people in the Delta were like people everywhere. He wanted Delta people to believe in themselves.

Name _____ Date _____

Performance Task 1
Part 1

Animals and Their Unique Abilities

Task:

Your science class takes a trip to the aquarium. A guide describes some underwater animals with amazing abilities like a mudskipper that climbs trees and a planarian that can heal itself. You and your classmates become interested in learning more about other animals with unique abilities. During your research, you found three more articles about this topic.

After you have looked at these sources, you will answer some questions about them. Briefly scan the sources and the three questions that follow. Then go back and read the sources carefully so you will have the information you need to answer the questions and complete your research. You may use scratch paper to take notes on information you find in the sources you read.

In Part 2, you will write a story using the information you read.

Directions for Beginning:

You will now look at several sources. You can look at any of the sources as often as you like.

Research Questions:

After reviewing the research sources, use the rest of the time in Part 1 to answer three questions about them. Your answers to these questions will be scored. Also, your answers will help you think about the information you read, which should help you write your narrative story.

You may refer back to your scratch paper to review your notes when you think it would be helpful. Answer the questions in the spaces below the items.

Your written notes on scratch paper will be available to you in Part 1 and Part 2 of the performance task.

Source #1

You found an article that describes how birds survive in the desert.

Desert Birds

Deserts are the driest places on Earth. They are also some of the hottest places. Yet some animals are able to live there. Certain birds are very good at adapting to the dry desert.

For example, the cactus wren can live with very little water. It uses its pointed beak to turn over rocks on the ground. Then it eats the insects underneath. From its food, it gets all the water it needs. The name *cactus wren* comes from where it lives. It lives in thorny trees and plants. The thorns are used to protect the cactus wren and its young from enemies.

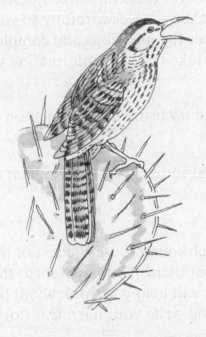

The roadrunner is another desert bird. It is famous for its ability to run very fast. It can travel at speeds as fast as 15 miles per hour. This desert bird is so quick it can catch a rattlesnake! It can also catch a dragonfly in the air! In fact, there's not much it won't eat. Rodents, lizards, and spiders are all favorite foods. The roadrunner uses its speed to catch its prey. But it also uses its speed to escape from enemies. It rarely flies, so being fast is important.

The roadrunner gets most of its water from eating other creatures, but it also has ways to make the most of its water supply. Water sources in the desert can be salty. Too much salt can be harmful. Luckily, this special bird has glands that remove salt from its body. The roadrunner rests during the hottest hours of the day. It does a lot of hunting in the cool evening. During this time, it needs less water.

A third desert bird is the sandgrouse. It deals with a lack of water in its own way. It will travel a long way to find a water source. While it drinks, the feathers on its belly will absorb and hold water. Then the sandgrouse will use these wet feathers to carry water. It brings the water to its chicks. It may travel as far as 75 miles to bring water to its chicks. This may happen a few times a day.

The sandgrouse is gray, brown, and beige. These are the colors of most desert birds. These colors allow it to hide in the desert. Under its feather cover is a thick layer of down. This protects the bird from extreme temperatures. When the desert becomes too hot or cold, the sandgrouse stays comfortable.

All these birds have qualities that make them unique. They have the ability to adapt to hard conditions.

Source #2
You found an article about animals that can change colors.

Quick Color Changes

A chameleon sitting among green leaves looks green. A chameleon resting on a tree trunk looks brown. A chameleon's skin color can change to match certain backgrounds. Blending in with a background is called camouflage. Chameleons are best known for their ability to change their look.

35

A chameleon's camouflage helps a chameleon hunt for insects. The camouflage also helps a chameleon hide from enemies. But these are not the main reason for changing colors. The main reason is that changing colors is a way to communicate. A chameleon in danger may suddenly turn black or change its pattern. This confuses its enemy. Male chameleons change to bright colors. They do this to warn off other males. Skin color changes can also show the animal's mood.

How does the chameleon's skin change color? The outer layer of skin is see-through. Under it are other layers with special cells. These special cells contain color. They grow or shrink depending on nerve and chemical signals in the chameleon's body.

The chameleon is a master of color change, but a different animal takes the prize for colorful tricks. It is the octopus.

A reddish octopus sits on the ocean floor. In an instant, it is gray. The next second, it is orange. The next moment, it is tan. These color changes are amazing to see. Some color changes mean the octopus is changing emotions. Other color changes help the octopus defend itself. The enemy sees the changing colors and becomes too shocked to attack. The octopus also uses color changes to hide from enemies. It can take on the colors of a sandy ocean bottom. It can combine colors to blend in with a patterned background. Some octopuses can change the texture of their skin from smooth to rough. They appear to be coral or rocks.

The colored cells in the octopus's skin have more parts than those in a chameleon. In an octopus, nerve signals act on the muscles around tiny sacs. The muscles squeeze or relax to open or close the sacs. This either reveals or hides the color. The octopus also has cells that reflect the light around it. In a way, the skin acts like a mirror. That explains why octopuses can take on the look of patterned backgrounds.

Source #3
You found an article about how monkeys can help people.

Monkey Helpers

Animals help people in a lot of ways. One amazing and helpful animal is the capuchin monkey. There are many things to help people in wheelchairs. For example, there are computer devices to help them with everyday tasks, but there are some things that a computer cannot do. That is where a monkey can help. A monkey has hands it can use to do things with. Other service animals do not have that ability.

Capuchin monkeys are from the tropical forests of Central and South America. These monkeys are about 1 to 2 feet long. They weigh between 2 and 9 pounds. They can live as long as 40 years in captivity. They are very intelligent. In the wild, these little monkeys use tools, such as sticks, to get food.

These monkeys can be trained to do small tasks. They can help people in wheelchairs be more independent. With the help of a capuchin monkey, people in wheelchairs can do things they would need another person to do.

In some ways, being a monkey trainer is like bringing up a baby. But a baby cannot climb the curtains and swing on them! Monkeys are very curious and like to explore. The monkey trainers have to keep their homes safe for monkeys. Monkeys can grab things that a small child could never get near.

Once the monkey reaches a certain skill level, it starts going to a training center. It attends classes four or five times a week. The monkeys learn to use their natural skills in different ways. They use their curious nature and love of handling objects. They go through more and more difficult training. When they finish a task, they receive a reward.

The monkeys learn about 30 commands. They learn to turn lights on and off. They learn to get something to eat or drink. They pick up dropped items. The monkeys can also help with books or voice recorders. They take things to the trash. They open and close a refrigerator. They even put a DVD in a player. Capuchins can help wash a person's face. They can also move a person's hand.

To learn to do these tasks, monkeys need lots of training. After that, the monkey is paired up with someone who needs help. The needs of the person are matched with the skills of the monkey. The monkeys become devoted to their new owners. And the new owners are devoted to their monkeys. The monkeys give people friendship and fun. Just because monkeys are helpers does not mean that they have forgotten how to play!

1 Source #1 and Source #2 discuss the unique abilities of some animals. Explain how animals use their unique abilities to survive. Use **one** detail from Source #1 and **one** detail from Source #2 to support your explanation. For each detail, include the source title or number.

_____

_____

_____

_____

2 Which source **most likely** has useful information about how animals can be trained? Explain why this source **most likely** has the most useful information about how animals can be trained. Give at least **two** details from the source to support your answer.

_____

_____

_____

_____

3 Mark the boxes to match each source with an idea or ideas that it supports. Some ideas may have more than one source selected.

	Source #1: Desert Birds	Source #2: Quick Color Changes	Source #3: Monkey Helpers
Some animals have developed special body features that help them adapt to their environment.			
Animals can develop relationships with people.			
Animals can communicate their emotions in different ways.			

Part 2

You will now review your notes and sources, and plan, draft, revise, and edit your writing. You may use your notes and go back to the sources. Now read your assignment and the information about how your writing will be scored, then begin your work.

Your Assignment:

Your teacher wants you to use the research information you gathered about unique animals. You are assigned to write a story that is several paragraphs long about a person who can take on the characteristics and abilities of the animals from your research.

In your story, you will choose two or three animals from the sources and write about how your character uses the abilities of those animals in an adventure story. Your character will face a big challenge or obstacle in your story. Describe how the person reacts and resolves the obstacle or challenge. When writing your story, find ways to use information and details from the sources to improve your story. Make sure you develop your characters, setting, and the plot. Also use details, dialogue, and description where appropriate.

REMEMBER: A well-written narrative story

- has an effective and complete plot.
- is well-organized and clear.
- has an introduction and conclusion.
- has a logical sequence of events.
- uses transitions.
- develops a setting, narrator/characters, and point of view.
- uses description, details, and dialogue.
- has effective and appropriate style.
- uses details from the sources to support your story.
- follows rules of writing (spelling, punctuation, grammar usage).

Name _____ Date _____

Now begin your work on your story. Manage your time carefully so that you can

- plan your multi-paragraph story.
- write your multi-paragraph story.
- revise and edit the final draft of your multi-paragraph story.

For Part 2, you are being asked to write a narrative story that is several paragraphs long. Write your response in the space below.

Remember to check your notes and your prewriting and planning as you write and then revise and edit your story.

_____

_____

_____

_____

_____

_____

_____

_____

_____

_____

_____

Name _____ Date _____

_____

_____

_____

_____

_____

_____

_____

_____

_____

_____

_____

_____

_____

_____

_____

_____

Name _____ Date _____

_____

_____

_____

_____

_____

_____

_____

_____

_____

_____

_____

_____

_____

_____

_____

_____

Assessment 2
Reading

Read the passage. Then answer the questions.

Aisha's Radio Play

"Good morning, class," said Mr. Calvin. "As you know, today is the last day to hand in plays for the fourth-grade playwriting contest. If you wish to enter a play, please hand it in by the end of the day. Tomorrow you'll form groups and practice your plays. Then, next week, you'll perform them for the class. There will be awards for best play, as well as for best sound effects, best characters, best props, and best costumes."

As Aisha listened to Mr. Calvin address the class, she thought about the radio play she had finished the night before. She was looking forward to turning in her play because she thought it was a unique idea. It was a hair-raising adventure story about two boys who get lost in the woods during a thunderstorm. Darkness is coming on, and in one scene, the kids imagine that a terrible monster is following them. Aisha had given her play a happy ending. Still, she wanted to have realistic sound effects for the scary parts, especially because radio plays are purely a sound performance, with no acting out scenes.

That evening Aisha sat at the family laptop. She prepared to download sound effects from the Internet. She planned to burn them onto a CD that she could take to class. She would then use the classroom computer to play her sound effects at various spots in her script. As she was waiting for the browser to load, her father came into the room and noticed she was waiting for the computer.

"I'm sorry, Aisha," he said. "Our Wi-Fi signal seems to be down. We think it may be a problem with our router. Your mother is phoning the Internet provider right now. She's been on hold for 20 minutes already, though."

"But I have to have sound effects for my radio play!" wailed Aisha.

"I wish I could help you, Aisha," said her father. "Right now, though, I need to finish making dinner. I need your help setting the table, too."

Name _____ Date _____

Aisha followed her father glumly, trying to think of a solution as she set the table. Gradually, she became aware of the sounds around her. Her little sister was running through the house, singing a rather tuneless song in her high voice. Her mother was drumming her fingers on a table somewhere as she waited on the phone for someone to take her call. Her father was clanging pots and pans on the stove and in the sink. Onions and peppers were sizzling in a pan on the stove. Aisha herself was clinking silverware. Her older brother, who was upstairs, suddenly started to practice on his drums, hitting the cymbals with a loud, crisp crash.

"That's it!" cried Aisha, throwing her arms open wide. "I'll make my own sound effects and record them." She ran back to the laptop. First, she reviewed her radio play, deciding what type of sound effects she would need. Next, she decided how to create each of her intended sound effects. Once she had resolved everything, she grabbed the laptop. With the help of her family after dinner, Aisha spent much of the evening recording sound effects for her play.

The next day as she left for school, her father said, "Break a leg!" Aisha smiled and headed to school. In class that day and in the days following, Aisha and her partner practiced and perfected their performance of Aisha's radio play. When they finally presented it to the class, everyone cheered. For many of them, it was their first time hearing a radio play. They were very impressed with what Aisha was able to do without using stage acting. As for the playwriting contest, Aisha's radio play won the award for best sound effects.

Name _____ Date _____

1 This question has two parts. First, answer part A. Then, answer part B.

Part A

According to the passage, how does Aisha feel about the playwriting contest?

Ⓐ She is unsure about the contest.

Ⓑ She is excited about the contest.

Ⓒ She is nervous about the contest.

Ⓓ She does not want to enter the contest.

Part B

Which sentence from the passage **best** supports the answer in part A?

Ⓐ She was looking forward to turning in her play because she thought it was a unique idea.

Ⓑ Gradually, she became aware of the sounds around her.

Ⓒ With the help of her family after dinner, Aisha spent much of the evening recording sound effects for her play.

Ⓓ When they finally presented it to the class, everyone cheered.

2 Read the sentences and the question that follows.

First, she reviewed her radio play, deciding what type of sound effects she would need. Next, she decided how to create each of her intended sound effects. Once she had <u>resolved</u> everything, she grabbed the laptop.

What does the word <u>resolved</u> **most likely** mean?

Ⓐ listed

Ⓑ erased

Ⓒ settled

Ⓓ accepted

Name _____ Date _____

3 Why is Aisha upset when she finds out that her family's Internet is not working?

Ⓐ She wants to finish typing her radio play.

Ⓑ She wants to present her radio play to her family.

Ⓒ She wants to upload her radio play to the website.

Ⓓ She wants to download sound effects for her radio play.

4 Underline the text from the passage that shows the author using an idiom.

> The next day as she left for school, her father said, "Break a leg!" Aisha smiled and headed to school. In class that day and in the days following, Aisha and her partner practiced and perfected their performance of Aisha's radio play. When they finally presented it to the class, everyone cheered. For many of them, it was their first time hearing a radio play. They were very impressed with what Aisha was able to do without using stage acting. As for the playwriting contest, Aisha's radio play won the award for best sound effects.

5 What makes Aisha decide to create her own sound effects? Support your answer with details from the passage.

_____

_____

_____

_____

Name _____ · Date _____

Read the passage. Then answer the questions.

Hear the Call

Thanks to the telephone, you or I can talk to a person in the next town. We can even talk to a person in another state or country. Of course, this technology has not always existed. Talking to each other was not always this easy to do. But people have always wanted to communicate with other people in faraway places.

Ancient Methods

Long ago, in ancient times, people used several methods to communicate over distances. People have been able to send written messages for thousands of years, but they have also wanted to communicate more quickly. Sometimes people would light fires. They would then use the smoke from the fire to send signals. People also beat drums and used the sound to communicate. Another popular system involved the use of flags to give visual signals. Unfortunately, most of these systems had problems. They were subject to the weather and other challenges, such as distance and visibility.

Telegraph

The telegraph uses electricity to send signals over wires or radio waves. The technology came into wide use in the mid-1800s. One of the early developers of the telegraph was Samuel Morse. He developed a system of dots and dashes that represented letters and numbers. Using a transmitter, the dots and dashes could be sent as signals over a wire. This became an important system for communication until the mid-1900s.

Telephones

The telephone was invented in the late 1800s by Alexander Graham Bell. It opened up new possibilities for personal communication. The telephone converts a person's voice into an electronic signal. Then it sends the signal over a wire from one end to the other. The telephone at the other end converts the signal back into the sound of the person's voice.

Early telephones had limitations that were overcome with time. The listening part of the telephone was held in the hand, while the speaking part was mounted on a base. The two parts were eventually combined into a single handset. In more recent times, telephones were made cordless.

Talking to someone without the handset was made possible through the use of speakers on the telephone. New features were added to the telephone such as call-waiting and voice-mail systems.

Cell Phones

The cell phone takes what is most effective about the telephone and makes it even better. The cell phone is a portable telephone. It also converts a person's voice into an electronic signal. It uses radio waves to send these signals between the cell phone and a cell tower. The signal is then relayed to another cell phone. The first cell phones were sold in Japan in 1979. They were first sold in the United States in 1983. Early cell phones were very expensive. They were also much larger than they are today. Technological developments soon made them less expensive. As a result, their popularity grew. By the 2000s, there were more cell phones in use than traditional telephones. Many people have both cell phones and traditional telephones. The cell phone eventually will take the place of the telephone.

The Future

The technology of personal communication has grown a great deal over the past 150 years. Given the change we have already seen, we might expect to see even more exciting developments in the near future. However, one thing will stay the same. People will always want to talk to other people, whether they are nearby or far away.

Sending Mail

For hundreds of years, letters were either delivered by messenger or passed from one person to another. To keep letters moving, they were passed to people who were traveling in the direction of the recipient. In 1639, a tavern in Boston became the first post office. It received letters that arrived from people overseas. It also accepted letters people dropped off there that were to be sent overseas. In 1775, Benjamin Franklin was appointed as the first postmaster.

Postage stamps were first introduced in the United States in 1847. However, it was not until 1855 that people had to pay for postage when

Name _____ Date _____

they dropped off mail. Until then, the person receiving the letter often had to pay. Mail was carried from one post office to another on foot or by horse. Beginning in 1862, rail was used, too. Airplanes were first used to transport mail in 1918.

People had to go to the post office to collect their letters. For people living far from town, that often meant a day trip just to get the mail. Joseph Briggs was a window clerk at a post office in Cleveland. In 1863, he had the idea of delivering mail to each house in the city. For this to happen, buildings had to be numbered, and street signs had to be put up. It was not until 1896 that the first rural routes were begun.

For many years, most written communication went through the post office. That changed when e-mail, or electronic mail, came into existence. By the 1970s, messages could be sent between computers in the same network. People who worked together could communicate with each other using e-mail. The @ symbol was adopted as part of the computer address.

In the late 1970s and 1980s, personal computers became available. Modern e-mail began. In the beginning, people could only communicate with others who had the same e-mail system.

Finally in 1989, people were able to directly access the Internet. Now they could use e-mail servers to communicate. An e-mail server acts much like a post office. It receives mail from the sender and delivers it to the recipient. Now anyone with a personal computer can send e-mail to any other person with a computer and an e-mail address. They do not need to be on the same network.

Today you need a computer or a mobile device, such as a cell phone or a tablet, and an Internet or a cell-phone connection to send an e-mail. You can be almost anywhere in the world and send an e-mail. You can attach photographs, videos, or documents to the e-mail. The message will be received almost instantly. E-mail is as fast as lightning. E-mail is free. People can send as many messages as they want. They can send messages to as many people as they want.

E-mail is much faster than regular mail. Regular mail is now sometimes called "snail mail." However, to use e-mail you have to pay for a computer or other device. Users also have to pay for an Internet or a cell-phone connection. These things can be expensive. E-mail can only be sent to people who have the necessary equipment and connection. But to send a regular letter, you only need a pen, an envelope, and a stamp. The post office delivers

Name _____ Date _____

letters to addresses throughout the world. Today, we have choices about how to send written communication. An e-mail is quick and easy, but is there anything better than seeing a handwritten envelope in your mailbox?

---

6 Read the paragraph from "Hear the Call."

> Long ago, in ancient times, people used several methods to communicate over distances. People have been able to send written messages for thousands of years, but they have also wanted to communicate more quickly. Sometimes people would light fires. They would then use the smoke from the fire to send signals. People also beat drums and used the sound to communicate. Another popular system involved the use of flags to give visual signals. Unfortunately, most of these systems had problems. They were subject to the weather and other challenges, such as distance and visibility.

Based on the paragraph from "Hear the Call," select **two** reasons why most ancient methods of communication had problems.

Ⓐ Loud drums bothered people.

Ⓑ Fire caused damage to nature.

Ⓒ Weather interfered with messages.

Ⓓ Radio waves were not strong enough.

Ⓔ Visual signals were difficult to see across long distances.

7 Read the sentences from "Hear the Call" and complete the task that follows.

> The telephone <u>converts</u> a person's voice into an electronic signal. Then it sends the signal over a wire from one end to the other.

What does the word <u>converts</u> mean as it is used in the sentence above?

Ⓐ drags

Ⓑ records

Ⓒ changes

Ⓓ squeezes

Name _____ Date _____

8 This question has two parts. First, answer part A. Then, answer part B.

Part A

Which text feature is used in "Hear the Call"?

Ⓐ graph

Ⓑ timeline

Ⓒ headings

Ⓓ table of contents

Part B

Why does the author use the text feature you chose in part A?

Ⓐ to show the relationship between traditional phones and cell phones

Ⓑ to show the order that the methods were used

Ⓒ to identify the topic of each paragraph

Ⓓ to identify different types of phones

9 Which **two** sentences from "Hear the Call" support the author's statement that "the cell phone eventually will take the place of the telephone"?

Ⓐ The cell phone is a portable telephone.

Ⓑ It uses radio waves to send these signals between the cell phone and a cell tower.

Ⓒ The first cell phones were sold in Japan in 1979.

Ⓓ Early cell phones were very expensive.

Ⓔ By the 2000s, there were more cell phones in use than traditional phones.

Name _____ Date _____

10 Read the sentence from the "Hear the Call" and the question that follows.

> The cell phone takes what is most <u>effective</u> about the telephone and makes it even better.

Which word has a similar meaning to the word <u>effective</u> as it is used in the sentence above?

Ⓐ useful

Ⓑ special

Ⓒ powerful

Ⓓ confusing

11 Read the sentences from "Sending Mail."

> Today you need a computer or a mobile device, such as a cell phone or a tablet, and an Internet or a cell-phone connection to send an e-mail. You can be almost anywhere in the world and send an e-mail. You can attach photographs, videos, or documents to the e-mail. The message will be received almost instantly. <u>E-mail is as fast as lightning</u>. E-mail is free. People can send as many messages as they want. They can send messages to as many people as they want.

Why does the author use the phrase "fast as lightning"?

Ⓐ to show that e-mail is shocking

Ⓑ to show that e-mail is not as fast as regular mail

Ⓒ to show that e-mail can be sent and received very quickly

Ⓓ to show that e-mail is sent using a computer and electricity

12 Read the paragraph from "Sending Mail." Underline the sentence that gives the best context for helping the reader understand the meaning of "snail mail."

> E-mail is much faster than regular mail. Regular mail is now sometimes called "snail mail." However, to use email you have to pay for a computer or other device. Users also have to pay for an Internet or a cell-phone connection. These things can be expensive. E-mail can only be sent to people who have the necessary equipment and connection. But to send a regular letter, you only need a pen, an envelope, and a stamp. The post office delivers letters to addresses throughout the world. Today, we have choices about how to send written communication. An e-mail is quick and easy, but is there anything better than seeing a handwritten envelope in your mailbox?

13 Which statement is a main idea of **both** "Hear the Call" and "Sending Mail"?

Ⓐ Technology has allowed us to send mail faster than we ever have before.

Ⓑ Cell phones provide the most convenient ways to communicate.

Ⓒ Cell phones are more practical than traditional phones.

Ⓓ Methods of communication continue to change.

14 Compare the author's purpose in "Hear the Call" and "Sending Mail." Is the author's purpose to entertain, persuade, or inform in each passage? Be sure to tell how the author's purpose for each passage is similar or different. Include examples from the passages to support your answer.

_____

_____

_____

_____

_____

15 Which of the following is an effect of advances in technology in **both** "Hear the Call" and "Sending Mail"?

ⓐ Communication is faster and more easily accessed.

ⓑ E-mails can be sent and received in seconds to places on the other side of the country.

ⓒ People can make phone calls from just about anywhere.

ⓓ People needed faster ways to communicate.

Read the passage. Then answer the questions.

The Visit

Sean's uncle Robert had come all the way from Scotland to visit. For his first American breakfast, Sean's mother gave Robert a bowl of hot oatmeal and whole wheat toast. "This porridge looks very appetizing indeed. Thank you, lassie," Uncle Robert said. "Porridge is actually a Scottish dish," he told Sean. "Many good things come from Scotland. I will tell you all about them."

That morning after breakfast, Sean and Uncle Robert took a stroll around the neighborhood. They talked about what it was like to grow up in Scotland, and his uncle told him great stories about the adventures of his youth. "Your winters seem to be a wee bit cold," Uncle Robert said. "We have cold days in Scotland, too, but not this bitter." Sean loved the way his uncle spoke, both the sound of his voice and the words he used.

Sean exclaimed, smiling, "I'm very glad you came in January. You'll be able to hear my school band play in the New Year's Variety Show next week. I play the clarinet."

Uncle Robert looked at him. "Not the bagpipes? How could you not play the bagpipes, the most impressive instrument in all of music? Your grandpa was the best bagpipe player in our village. He played at each and every festival." Sean looked at his uncle, surprised, and whispered, "I've never even seen a bagpipe in real life!"

Several days later, the entire family thoroughly enjoyed the New Year's Variety Show, especially the clarinet playing. After the show they enjoyed dinner together at a restaurant in town. In fact, Sean enjoyed everything about his visit with Uncle Robert; too bad he had to return to Scotland just a few days after the show. A few weeks after Uncle Robert left, a large box arrived for Sean. He carefully opened the package, wondering what it could be. He discovered that Uncle Robert had sent him his own set of bagpipes! Sean thought they were absolutely beautiful and gazed at them in awe.

Name _____ Date _____

Sean was thrilled and couldn't wait to learn how to play. He already played a wind instrument, so the bagpipes couldn't be too difficult. He asked his music teacher, "Could I learn to play a song on the bagpipes by next year's show? Uncle Robert is coming back to visit us then. I'd really love to surprise him."

"Playing the bagpipes takes a lot of hard work and patience," explained his teacher. "I can't teach you to play, but I know a very good music teacher who can. I think you can do it if you work hard and stay focused."

Sean did just that; he worked hard for one whole year. He was careful when handling the bagpipes. He practiced every day and never abandoned his efforts. He began with a practice chanter, which looks a bit like a recorder. After some months he graduated to a "goose," a small, simple bagpipe. At first he could play it for only a few minutes before feeling dizzy and winded! He persisted, however, and gradually he increased his lungpower and strength. In time he could play several tunes without feeling weak or dizzy at all.

When Uncle Robert returned for a visit, Sean was ready to surprise him with a song. The school choir opened the variety show with a performance of "America the Beautiful." Then Sean's friend Sal recited all thirteen stanzas of "The Midnight Ride of Paul Revere." Next, a fifth-grader recited a speech by a character in a scene from a famous movie. Then, the third-graders played a patriotic song on their recorders. Finally, it was Sean's turn to perform for the audience. He walked to center stage with his bagpipes. "Tonight I am welcoming the New Year and my Uncle Robert with a Scottish song," he announced. "I will play 'Scotland Forever' in memory of my grandfather who was one of the finest pipers in all of Scotland."

Sean began to play his bagpipes. The crowd looked enthusiastic and watched with undivided attention. A few children danced along to his song. But Sean looked out into the crowd and saw only his family. Most importantly, in the third row center, a very pleased Uncle Robert was smiling a cheerful smile from ear to ear! Sean was full of excitement while he played and knew his uncle was, too.

Name _____ Date _____

16 Read the dictionary entry.

> bitter [**bit**-er] *adjective* **1.** having a harsh taste. **2.** hard
> to admit or accept. **3.** resentful or cynical. *adverb* **4.**
> extremely; very.

Read the sentence from the passage.

"We have cold days in Scotland, too, but not this <u>bitter</u>."

Which meaning **best** fits the way the word <u>bitter</u> is used in
the sentence?

Ⓐ meaning 1

Ⓑ meaning 2

Ⓒ meaning 3

Ⓓ meaning 4

17 This question has two parts. First, answer part A. Then, answer
part B.

Part A

How does Uncle Robert feel listening to Sean play the bagpipes?

Ⓐ happy

Ⓑ nervous

Ⓒ displeased

Ⓓ disappointed

Part B

Read the paragraph from "The Visit." Underline the **four** words in
the paragraph that support the answer in part A.

But Sean looked out into the crowd and saw only his family. Most
importantly, in the third row center, a very pleased Uncle Robert
was smiling a cheerful smile from ear to ear! Sean was full of
excitement while he played and knew his uncle was, too.

Name _____ Date _____

18 Why does Sean think the bagpipes will not be difficult to learn?

  Ⓐ His grandfather played the bagpipes.

  Ⓑ He already played a wind instrument.

  Ⓒ His uncle said it would be easy to learn.

  Ⓓ His music teacher told him it would be easy to learn.

19 Read the sentences and the question that follows.

  He was careful when handling the bagpipes. He practiced every day and never <u>abandoned</u> his efforts.

  Which **two** words have the **opposite** meaning of the <u>underlined</u> word?

  Ⓐ left

  Ⓑ quit

  Ⓒ gave up

  Ⓓ escaped

  Ⓔ stayed on

  Ⓕ continued

20 Label each event from the story in the order in which it happened. The first event will be labeled 1, and the last event will be labeled 5.

  ___ Uncle Robert sends Sean a set of bagpipes from Scotland.

  ___ Sean plays "Scotland Forever" at the New Year's Variety Show.

  ___ Sean decides to surprise Uncle Robert with a bagpipe tune the next year.

  ___ Uncle Robert hears Sean play the clarinet in the New Year's Variety Show.

  ___ Sean practices the difficult instrument for a year.

Writing

Read and answer each question.

21 Emilia is writing a story for her class about her vacation. Read the paragraph from the draft of her story. Underline the **two** words that contain mistakes in spelling.

> Once we reached Florida, we headed directly to the beach. My parents stayed in their beach chairs, so just the too of us played in the sand. My brother and I built sand castles and swam in the ocean. We saw colorful fish and even a few dolphins! I was so glad I could capture every moment. My parents' camera came in vary handy. I snapped so many pictures my fingers began to hurt.

22 Choose the sentence that contains a spelling error.

Ⓐ The birds were singing loudly in the morning.

Ⓑ I decorated the cake with green and blue flowers.

Ⓒ He trained every day and gained strength in his arms.

Ⓓ The neighbors on our block are freindlier than the ones on your block.

23 Underline the word in the paragraph that has a spelling error.

> Julia looked at the envelopes in Mr. Peter's hand. The report cards were here. Julia was excited to see her grades. She heard her classmates nervusly tapping on their desks. Mr. Peter called each student's name aloud. Finally, it was Julia's turn.

24 A student is writing a report about fire safety. The paragraph needs an introduction to the topic. Read the paragraph and complete the task that follows.

> First, every person needs to know two ways out of the house at all times. Second, each home should have a smoke detector. One should be on every floor. Third, every family needs to agree on a meeting place outside the house. The most important number to remember is 911. When family members work together to keep their home safe, accidents don't have to become disasters.

Which sentence could be added in the beginning of the paragraph to introduce the topic?

Ⓐ Fires can be prevented with a few simple steps.

Ⓑ In emergencies, remember to rescue any animals.

Ⓒ Stop, drop, and roll in the event of a house fire.

Ⓓ Fire safety is an important part about living at home.

25 Which sentence has an error in grammar usage?

Ⓐ Sharon has spoken to her teacher already.

Ⓑ Brent spent all of his money on the game.

Ⓒ Jody is leaving the party yesterday night.

Ⓓ Sam and Jose are skiing too close to the cliff.

26 Which sentence is correct?

Ⓐ We didn't see him, he saw us.

Ⓑ John was surprised, he got a letter in the mail.

Ⓒ She studied for hours, but she did not pass the test.

Ⓓ I wore a coat, because it was supposed to be cold today.

27 Hector is writing a report about comets. Read the draft of his first paragraph and complete the task that follows.

> Comets are fascinating for many reasons. For example, comets are leftover rocks from planets when the solar system was formed. We usually call them shooting stars. They are made mostly of ice and travel around the Sun. Comets develop tails near the Sun. When they're too close, they cause a water-like streak in the sky.

The last sentence of the paragraph is not the best ending. Which sentence should move to the **end** of the story?

ⒶComets are fascinating for many reasons.

ⒷWe usually call them shooting stars.

ⒸThey are made mostly of ice and travel around the Sun.

ⒹComets develop tails near the Sun.

28 The following is the beginning of an opinion article that a student is writing for the school newspaper. The article needs more support for why more hours should be added to the school day. Read the beginning of the article and complete the task that follows.

> The school day should be extended by one or two hours. Adding more hours to the school day will help the daily lives of students. Students would have more time to do schoolwork. They could also receive help from teachers. Teachers would have more flexibility to cover different topics and subjects. Making this change will definitely make students' lives happier.

Choose **two** sentences that support the opinions in the paragraph.

ⒶTeachers will have more time to use creative ideas in lessons and projects.

ⒷParents will have to rearrange their schedules to adjust to the time change.

ⒸParents will not have to hire tutors if more class time is given in the day.

ⒹMany students have other responsibilities outside of their school day.

ⒺMany students want to spend more time with their families.

Name _____ Date _____

29 A fourth-grade book club is reading a book about saving the rain forests. A club member is writing her summary of the book for the class. Read the paragraph and complete the task that follows.

(1) We are losing the rain forests. (2) Nearly one-half of all rain forests are being lost. (3) Most are being cleared by bulldozers owned by big companies. (4) Some species will be extinct if the rain forests are gone. (5) The Amazon rain forest is the largest rain forest on Earth. (6) It has been described as the "Lungs of our Planet." (7) Fewer rain forests mean less oxygen and clean air.

The student wants to add another detail after sentence 6 in the paragraph. Which sentence should the student add?

Ⓐ The Amazon rain forest is home to 10 percent of the world's known species.

Ⓑ A lot of dangerous species like the anaconda live in the Amazon rain forest.

Ⓒ Over half of the Amazon rain forest is located in South American countries.

Ⓓ More than 20 percent of the world's oxygen is produced in the Amazon rain forest.

Name _____ Date _____

30 A student is writing an opinion paper about homework. Read the paragraphs and write an introduction for this paper.

Many students believe homework should be removed. The stress produced from homework can harm students' health. It can also harm their family life. With too much homework, students can become exhausted. They may not want to do any work. The stress can also strain family relationships.

Also, students lose time for other activities. With too much homework, it is difficult for students to find time for sports, music, or art.

Today's research shows that homework is not that effective. Many teachers are assigning homework that does not benefit student learning.

_____

_____

_____

_____

Listening

Listen to the presentation. Then answer the questions.

The Return of the Wolf

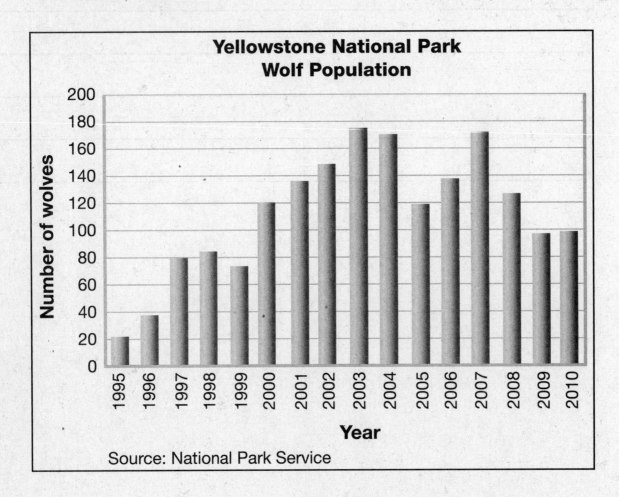

Name _____ Date _____

31 What does the author hope the listener will learn from the presentation? Select **two** responses.

Ⓐ how many zoos take in wolves

Ⓑ which law protects wolves today

Ⓒ why it's expensive to raise wolves

Ⓓ why wolves were endangered in America

Ⓔ how settlers and farmers lived in the West

Ⓕ which animals are on the endangered species list

32 What is the **most likely** reason the author made the presentation?

Ⓐ to give an example of how the state and government work with one another

Ⓑ to describe the efforts that were made to save wolves from disappearing

Ⓒ to prove that wolves are a problem because they hunt other animals

Ⓓ to teach a lesson on the history of how wolves first came to America

33 The government was successful in helping wolves survive in their natural habitat. Which detail from the presentation **best** supports this conclusion?

Ⓐ State programs released wolves that were raised in zoos.

Ⓑ Certain wilderness areas were designated off-limits to people.

Ⓒ Almost 100 wolves live in Yellowstone National Park today.

Ⓓ Wolf packs traveled throughout North America thousands of years ago.

Listen to the presentation. Then answer the questions.

When Tsunamis Strike

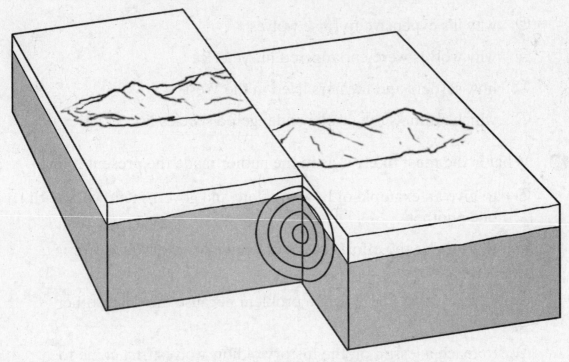

Name _____ Date _____

34 The following question has two parts. First, answer part A. Then, answer part B.

Part A

Which conclusion is supported by the presentation?

Ⓐ The waves of a tsunami always travel fast.

Ⓑ Tsunamis rarely cause any harm to people.

Ⓒ Some natural disasters can cause a tsunami.

Ⓓ The height of tsunami waves depends on weather.

Part B

Which detail from the presentation supports the answer in part A?

Ⓐ Tsunamis are caused by earthquakes, landslides, or volcanoes.

Ⓑ Tsunami waves are powerful enough to destroy property.

Ⓒ Tsunami waves can reach great heights close to land.

Ⓓ Tsunamis can move at high speeds in deep water.

35 What is the **most likely** purpose of the presentation? Select **two** responses.

Ⓐ to inform people about the nature of tsunamis

Ⓑ to give an example of a tsunami in real time

Ⓒ to teach a lesson on the beauty of tsunamis

Ⓓ to prove that tsunamis are faster than jets

Ⓔ to describe how a tsunami is formed

36 It is difficult to spot tsunamis in deep open water. Which detail from the presentation **best** supports this conclusion?

Ⓐ Tsunami waves are not very tall when the water is deep.

Ⓑ Tsunami waves travel at 500 to 600 miles per hour in deep water.

Ⓒ Tsunamis move outward from an epicenter of a disturbance.

Ⓓ Tsunamis are caused by movements in the Earth's crust.

Listen to the presentation. Then answer the questions.

Butterflies

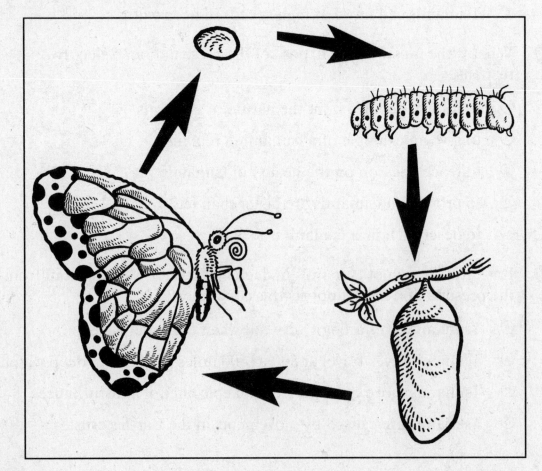

37 What is the presentation **mostly** about?

Ⓐ butterflies that lay eggs

Ⓑ ants that like sweet liquid

Ⓒ ants and butterflies that live in the wild

Ⓓ ants and butterflies that help one another

38 Mark the boxes to show which insect, ant or caterpillar, is responsible for each task in the process.

	Ant	Caterpillar
Chews flowers		
Carries insect back to nest		
Uses silk thread		
Tastes sweet liquid		
Turns into butterfly		

39 Which conclusion is supported by the presentation?

Ⓐ Ants like all types of sweet liquid.

Ⓑ Caterpillars live longer as butterflies.

Ⓒ Ants and caterpillars are close friends.

Ⓓ Caterpillars use their enemies to survive.

Research

Read and answer each question.

40 A student is writing a research report about dogs with service jobs. Underline the sentence that has information that the student can use in her report about therapy dogs.

> Many dogs are considered working dogs. Some dogs work with the police as K-9 officers. Others work as search and rescue dogs. Other dogs work with individuals. A Seeing Eye dog helps people with vision impairments. Another type of dog visits with people who are sick and in the hospital or who have just been through a traumatic event.

41 A student is writing a research report about Martin Luther King Jr. She wrote the following opinion: Dr. Martin Luther King Jr. was a very influential man in the civil rights movement. She found a source. Read the source. Then underline the **two** sentences that are **least** helpful in supporting the opinion.

> Martin finished school early and became a minister. After graduating from college he met and married Coretta Scott. In 1963 Dr. Martin Luther King Jr. led a march called the March on Washington. He was leading more than 200,000 people to the nation's capital to spread his message. This march is where he gave his famous "I Have a Dream" speech. This speech moved many people to support his civil rights movement. Changes started happening across the country. New laws were passed giving black people more rights.

42 A student is writing a report about the environment. She found a table with information about landfills. Read the table and complete the task that follows.

**Time It Takes for Materials
to Disintegrate/ Break Down in Landfills**

Plastic	Paper	Tin Cans
100–1,000 years	2–5 months	50–100 years

The student found a second source. Statements from the second source are found below.

> Landfills are filling up quickly in our country. The items in landfills will not all break down very quickly. Plastic bags, bottles, and other items left in landfills stay there for thousands of years. Recycling is imperative to the future of our environment. A lot of people already recycle paper products. It is important that more people start recycling more products.

Which detail from the second source supports the information in the table?

Ⓐ Landfills are filling up quickly in our country.

Ⓑ A lot of people already recycle paper products.

Ⓒ Recycling is imperative to the future of our environment.

Ⓓ Plastic bags, bottles, and other items left in landfills stay there for thousands of years.

43 A student made a plan for a research report. Read the plan and complete the task that follows.

Research Report Plan

Topic: coral reefs

Audience: students in science class/teacher

Purpose: to inform

Research Question: What types of animals live in coral reefs?

The student found a source for the research report.

> Large areas of coral are called coral reefs. Coral reefs are home to fierce predators such as sharks. Reef animals need to have ways to protect themselves. Some sea creatures need help from other animals to survive. The reef protects some animals. It also provides food for some animals. Angelfish eat sponges, which live on the coral.

Which **two** sentences from the source have information that answers the research question?

Ⓐ Large areas of coral are called coral reefs.

Ⓑ Coral reefs are home to fierce predators such as sharks.

Ⓒ Reef animals need to have ways to protect themselves.

Ⓓ Some sea creatures need help from other animals to survive.

Ⓔ Angelfish eat sponges, which live on the coral.

44 A student is writing a research report about the human body. She wrote the following opinion: The nervous system is the most important system in the human body. She found a source: *The Human Body* by Chloe Davidson.

> The human body has many important systems. The brain controls the nervous system, which affects every part of your body. The heart is part of the circulatory system. The heart pumps blood throughout the body. Muscles are important for both the muscular system and the skeletal system. Sensory nerves allow you to use all your senses; without them you couldn't smell, taste, hear, touch, or see. The digestive system allows us to eat and digest food so we can have energy throughout the day.

Select the **two** sentences that support the opinion.

Ⓐ The brain controls the nervous system, which affects every part of your body.

Ⓑ The heart pumps blood throughout the body.

Ⓒ Muscles are important for both the muscular system and the skeletal system.

Ⓓ Sensory nerves allow you to use all your senses; without them you couldn't smell, taste, hear, touch, or see.

Ⓔ The digestive system allows us to eat and digest food so we can have energy throughout the day.

Performance Task 2

Part 1

Earth's Changing Climate

Task:

Your class recently took a trip to the zoo, where you learned that some animals have adaptations that help them survive in different environments and climates. Some of those animals deal easily with climate change, while other animals struggle. You become interested in climate change and its causes and effects. You find three sources about this topic in the school library.

After you have reviewed these sources, you will answer some questions about them. Briefly scan the sources and the three questions that follow. Then go back and read the sources carefully so you will have the information you will need to answer the questions and complete your research. You may use scratch paper to take notes on the information you find in the sources as you read.

In Part 2, you will write an opinion essay about climate change.

Directions for Beginning:

You will now look at several sources. You can look at any of the sources as often as you like.

Research Questions:

After reviewing the research sources, use the rest of the time in Part 1 to answer three questions about them. Your answers to these questions will be scored. Also, your answers will help you think about the information you read, which should help you write your opinion essay.

You may refer back to your scratch paper to review your notes when you think it would be helpful. Answer the questions in the spaces below the items.

Your written notes on scratch paper will be available to you in Part 1 and Part 2 of the performance task.

Source #1
You have found an article that describes the changes Earth's climate has gone through over time.

Earth's Climate Cycles

Right now, Earth is a comfortable place for the living things that inhabit it. In some places, it may get a little too hot or cold, or it may be a little too dry or wet, but mostly the weather is suited to people and animals.

This hasn't always been true. Earth's climate has changed many times before. At times, most of the planet was covered in ice. At other times, it has been much warmer. Over at least the last 650,000 years, temperatures and carbon dioxide levels in the atmosphere have increased and decreased. This cycle takes thousands of years.

There are many reasons Earth's climate has changed in the past. Earth's orbit changes slightly which means Earth may be a bit closer or farther away from the Sun. This change happens over tens of thousands of years. For the last few thousand years, we've been in a relatively warmer period. At other times in Earth's history, the Sun has given off more energy. This has warmed Earth.

Different gases in the atmosphere also affect the temperature. About two billion years ago, Earth was much hotter. It also contained much more carbon dioxide. Then photosynthesis began. Photosynthesis uses carbon dioxide and releases oxygen. This cooled Earth.

Volcanoes can also cause climate change. Long ago during Earth's early history, very active volcanoes added a lot of carbon dioxide to the atmosphere. This caused the planet to get warmer. Today volcanic gases can cause Earth to get warmer or cooler. The temperature change depends on how sunlight interacts with the gases.

When scientists talk about climate change, they mean changes in average temperature over time. This is not a day-to-day change. Earth has warmed by about 1 degree Fahrenheit over the past 100 years. They say natural factors that could be causing this are changes in the Sun's energy level and Earth's orbit.

These climate changes can cause more extreme weather and affect animal habitats. Scientists say Earth is already seeing some of these changes.

Source #2

You have found an article that describes the effects of climate change on sea animals.

Climate Change and Sea Animals

The oceans contain many unique environments, including coral reefs. There are many coral reefs in the world. They are made up of tiny animals called corals. Corals live in large groups. These groups can contain millions of animals. Corals are actually soft but they build limestone skeletons outside their bodies. They do this by taking calcium out of the seawater. These rocky skeletons create hard, colorful reefs.

Coral reefs are found in oceans around the world. The Great Barrier Reef is the most amazing reef in the world. It is the largest coral reef on Earth. The reef is made up of more than 2,800 reefs. It stretches more than 1,200 miles. It can be found between 10 to 100 miles off the coast of Australia.

The Great Barrier Reef is home to many different kinds of animals. Many do not live anywhere else. There are hundreds of kinds of coral. Countless number of sea animals also depend on the reef to live. Many fish and birds also depend on the reef.

Unfortunately, this wonderful reef is in danger. The special animals that depend on the reef are in danger, too. There are many reasons for this. One is the rising temperature of the sea. This is caused by climate change. Scientists mainly agree that people's actions have sped up natural changes in climate. More than 100 years ago, people around the world started burning large amounts of coal, oil, and natural gas. They used these fuels to power their homes, factories, and vehicles.

Today, most of the world relies on these fossil fuels for their energy needs. Burning fossil fuels releases carbon dioxide. This gas traps heat. Corals are sensitive to even 1 degree Celsius rises in temperature. Tiny animals that live inside the coral reef help the corals to get oxygen and food. When the water warms, the tiny animals no longer live inside the coral reef. Warmer water also may make it easier for deadly diseases to live. They then infect the coral.

Another reef animal that struggles in warmer water is the sea turtle. Some sea turtles look for food in coral reefs. With the reefs in danger, the turtles are, too. Sea turtles also face danger from rising sea levels and temperatures. The turtles come to the beach to lay eggs. The sand is hotter because the water is hotter. Eggs will not hatch if it is too hot.

Although there are fewer sea turtles, scientists hope that they will survive. Scientists believe that can happen because sea turtles have been on Earth for more than 100 million years. They have lived through a lot of climate change already. The turtles might survive by moving to cooler water or finding new beaches.

Source #3

You found an article that discusses climate change and how scientists have been surprised by adaptations that two animals have made.

Adaptation and Climate Change

Scientists are concerned about climate change. They say people are speeding up the warming of the planet. This changes the environment for all living creatures. For example, when too much ice melts in the Arctic, animals that are adapted to snow have trouble hunting or hiding from predators. Polar bears rest on ice. If they have less ice, then they have to swim longer distances. Most researchers believe that change is happening too fast for many species to keep up. Some animals are able to adapt.

Others cannot. Some scientists believe that past climate changes may have caused animals that could not adapt to become extinct.

Scientists try to predict what will happen. They also try to understand what is happening now. The more information they have, the better. For example, polar bears have begun looking for food in Arctic villages and hunting camps. They have also begun to leave the ice earlier in spring. This means that they overlap with the nesting season of Arctic geese and ducks. The bears are eating the birds' eggs. While eggs are nutritious, they are not enough food for the big bears.

Scientists do not understand everything about how animals can adapt. Some animals may be able to adjust when they migrate or have babies. Others may be able to move to cooler areas as Earth warms. Some others may not be able to adapt quickly enough.

Many scientists are studying climate change. Some of the news is bad, but there is a little good news. Some studies have given scientists hope.

In one study, butterflies did better than scientists expected them to do. Certain butterflies are sensitive to rising temperatures. They live in Southern California, which is getting hotter. Scientists thought the butterflies would not be able to survive. They thought the butterflies would not be able to fly north to get to a cooler place. The butterflies adapted by moving to higher areas. In these areas, the temperatures are lower. The butterflies also learned to lay their eggs on plants that grow in their new environment.

Another animal that is doing better than expected are corals. Corals are also sensitive to rising temperatures. Corals lose their color in the heat. That is because they spit out algae in hot water. Algae gives corals their color. It also helps corals collect energy. One study found that over time, corals learned how to live in warmer water.

One type of owl that lives in northern Europe is also showing signs of change. The tawny owl can be light gray or brown. Light gray is the best camouflage in the snow. The average amount of snow in Finland is going down. As that happens, scientists have been seeing more brown tawny owls.

No one knows exactly what will happen in the future. Scientists are always learning new things. Climate change is affecting our planet, but some of the animals that live on Earth may surprise us with their adaptability.

81

1 Source #1 discusses how the Earth's climate changes naturally over time and the possible causes of this climate change. Explain how Source #2 adds to the understanding of the effects of climate change. Give two details from Source #2 to support your explanation.

_____

_____

_____

_____

2 Which source would **most likely** be the most helpful in understanding how animals adapt to climate change? Explain why this source is **most likely** the most helpful. Use **two** details from the source to support your explanation.

_____

_____

_____

_____

3 Mark the boxes to match the sources with the information found in the article.

	Source #1: Earth's Climate Cycles	Source #2: Climate Change and Sea Animals	Source #3: Adaptation and Climate Change
The Earth's climate has been changing since the beginning of time.			
There are many reasons for Earth's changing climate.			
Some animals may be able to adapt to change better than scientists first believed.			

Part 2

You will now review your notes and sources, and plan, draft, revise, and edit your writing. You may use your notes and go back to the sources. Now read your assignment and the information about how your writing will be scored, then begin your work.

Your Assignment:

Your teacher wants students to form an opinion and write an article about one thing that interested them about climate change. You will use the three sources to explain if you think climate change is caused by people or is natural. Your article will be read by other students, teachers, and parents.

Using more than one source, develop an opinion about climate change. Choose the most important information that supports your opinion. Then write an article that explains why you think the way you do about the causes of climate change. Clearly organize your article and support your opinion with details from the sources. Use your own words except when quoting directly from the sources. Be sure to give the source title or number when using details from the sources.

REMEMBER: A well-written opinion article

- has a clear statement of opinion.
- is well organized and stays on topic.
- has an introduction and a conclusion.
- uses transitions.
- uses details from the sources to support your opinion.
- puts the information from the sources in your own words, except when using direct quotations from the sources.
- gives the title or number of the source for the details or facts you included.
- develops ideas clearly.
- uses clear language.
- follows rules of writing (spelling, punctuation, and grammar usage).

Now begin work on your opinion article. Manage your time carefully so that you can

    1. plan your opinion article.

    2. write your opinion article.

    3. revise and edit the final draft of your opinion article.

For Part 2, you are being asked to write an opinion article that is several paragraphs long. Write your response in the space below.

Remember to check your notes and your prewriting and planning as you write, and then review and edit your opinion article.

_____

_____

_____

_____

_____

_____

_____

_____

_____

_____

_____

Name _____ Date _____

Name _____ Date _____

Assessment 3
Reading

Read the passage. Then answer the questions.

Kira's Library

Every bookshelf in Kira Green's bedroom was overflowing with books! Kira loved reading, and because her collection of books, magazines, and comic books was so enormous, it wouldn't fit on her shelves. She didn't want to get rid of any of them, so Kira stacked some things beside the window, then she shoved some of the books under her bed to get them out of the way.

Although Kira was very proud of her collection, it had gotten to the point that whenever she wanted to read something, it was practically impossible to find! Kira decided she had to get organized. She started by sorting her magazines, which is what she was doing when she heard footsteps coming up the stairs.

Just then, Kira's mother walked into her room and asked, "Where are you, Kira?"

"I'm right here," Kira said, popping her head out from behind a towering pile of magazines.

"We have a big problem here, Kira," Mrs. Green said, looking upset.

"I know. I know. I need to get more bookshelves and straighten out this mess!" Kira answered.

"There's no space in here for any more bookshelves," Mrs. Green said. "In fact, I think it's time for you to get rid of some of these books. Maybe you could donate some."

"I can't donate them to strangers, Mom; these are my favorites!" Kira cried.

"Well," said Mrs. Green, "unfortunately all this stuff is becoming hazardous, so you'll need to figure out a different solution."

Kira was in a pickle! While she didn't want to give away her books, she knew her mother was right. Her collection had taken over her bedroom, and there was no other storage space in their apartment for it.

The next day during lunch, Kira asked her friends to help her brainstorm ideas. "Maybe you could sell your comic books and earn some money," Andrea suggested.

"What about adding another room to your apartment?" Paul asked.

"I don't want to sell my comics, and you can't just add a room to an apartment," Kira replied.

After a few moments of silence, Andrea suggested that they think about it separately and meet outside the library after school. *That's it! The library. That's my solution!* Kira thought, smiling. For the rest of the day the wheels were spinning in her mind. She had a plan, and she was working out all the details, getting more excited as the day went on.

"I've figured out what to do," Kira announced when she saw Andrea and Paul later that afternoon. "I'm going to begin my own book club that will function like a library. I'll bring some of my books and magazines to school, and our friends and classmates can borrow my books, magazines, and comics for free," Kira explained. "And if enough people borrow my books each week, then I will always have enough room! I'll have some for my neighbors to borrow, too. This is going to be great!"

To help Kira get started, family and friends arranged her collection into categories and made a list of every book, magazine, and comic book. Then they put a label inside each item and helped Kira decide which ones to loan out first. She came up with a rotation system that would be easy for her to manage. They were ready to be loaned to friends and neighbors.

Kira talked to her teacher about loaning the books and magazines to the kids at school. She loved the idea. Kira's teacher allowed her to spend several minutes each morning lending books and magazines to her classmates. On the first day, Kira's classmates lined up eagerly. "Hey, Kira," called Jack, "do you have the latest issue of *Adventure* magazine?"

"I certainly do!" she said.

"I can't believe I get to read all this awesome stuff for free," Jack commented. Other students also talked excitedly about the books and how generous it was of Kira to let her friends borrow them.

Kira was thrilled. Her club was off to a great start, and she was helping her classmates at the same time! Even better, she didn't have to get rid of a single book!

Name _____ Date _____

1 What is the meaning of the idiom "in a pickle" as it is used in the passage?

Ⓐ   in a small space

Ⓑ   sad and confused

Ⓒ   scared or nervous

Ⓓ   in a difficult situation

2 What is a theme of the passage?

Ⓐ   The library is a great place to find books.

Ⓑ   You should always keep your bedroom organized.

Ⓒ   Sometimes you can help yourself by helping others.

Ⓓ   Friends can help you find a solution to your problems.

3 Which word used in the passage has the suffix that means "in a certain way"?

Ⓐ   sorting

Ⓑ   collection

Ⓒ   announced

Ⓓ   unfortunately

4 Which **two** words in the first paragraph help the reader understand the setting and problem of the passage?

Ⓐ   overflowing

Ⓑ   magazines

Ⓒ   stacked

Ⓓ   shelves

Ⓔ   window

Ⓕ   shoved

5 How have Kira's feelings about her large book collection changed from the beginning of the story to the end of the story? Support your answer with details from the passage.

_____

_____

_____

_____

Name _____ Date _____

Read the passage. Then answer the questions.

The Unstoppable Clara Barton

Clara Barton was born in 1821 in Massachusetts. She was a bright and independent child. She was also somewhat shy. Her father had been in the Army and told Clara stories of his time serving. Her older brother David had a bad fall from the roof when he was building a barn. After the accident he was too weak to care for himself. Clara cared for him and discovered her talent for helping those in need. When she was still a teenager, she became a teacher. She later opened a public school in New Jersey.

In 1861, when the Civil War broke out, Clara went to work helping wounded soldiers. Initially she collected and distributed supplies for the Army. She used her own money to buy food, clothing, and other supplies. She turned the limited supplies into nutritious meals, comforted the patients, and made sure they had water.

In 1862, Clara began assisting surgeons in dangerous battlefield conditions. She got so close to battle that she was once shot through the sleeve. She soon proved extremely useful by developing quick, effective systems to help as many soldiers as possible. Her triage system is still used today. It helps doctors treat the most needy patients first. The system has three levels: those who need immediate care, those who can wait a little while, and those who can wait hours or days.

Clara worked tirelessly at a total of 16 battle sites. She became known as the "angel of the battlefield." She had two guiding principles during the war. The first principle was "unconcern for what cannot be helped." She would not spend time trying to deal with situations that could not be improved. It was not that she didn't care about the cases that could not be improved. She knew that to help as many people as possible she needed to move on to those she could help. The second principle was "control under pressure." No matter what was going on around her, Clara stayed calm and carried out her responsibilities.

After the Civil War ended in 1865, Clara worked for the United States War Department. She tracked down information about missing soldiers and helped to reunite soldiers with their families. She also became a lecturer, giving public talks. Her talks about her experiences in the war were very popular. Her heroism and hard work on the battlefields became known throughout the country.

Name _____ Date _____

While she was visiting Europe, Clara learned about the International Red Cross, an organization that was established to help people in times of war. She set out to establish an American branch of this organization. Its focus would be not only on war but also peacetime disasters, such as floods, earthquakes, and famines. In 1881, as a result of her efforts, the American Red Cross became a reality. Clara became its first president. During her time with the American Red Cross, she oversaw aid for victims of disasters such as the Johnstown Flood in Pennsylvania in 1889 and the Galveston Flood in Texas in 1900.

Clara Barton headed the American Red Cross for 23 years, until she was 91 years old. Today, monuments honor her work during the Civil War and her life of service. One of the monuments built in her honor is at Antietam National Battlefield in Maryland. Another such monument can be found at her final home in Glen Echo, Maryland.

---

6 What event helped Clara Barton discover her gift for helping others?

ⓐ She opened a school.

ⓑ The Civil War began.

ⓒ She assisted surgeons on the battlefield.

ⓓ She cared for her brother after he had an accident.

7 What did Clara Barton do **after** the Civil War ended that made her actions well known?

ⓐ She called herself "the angel of the battlefield."

ⓑ She took care of her brother after his accident.

ⓒ She had several monuments built in her honor.

ⓓ She gave public talks about her experiences on the battlefield.

8 Which structure does the author use in the passage?

Ⓐ Sequence

Ⓑ Description

Ⓒ Problem and Solution

Ⓓ Compare and Contrast

9 Underline the word that means <u>a group of people that join together for a purpose.</u>

> She set out to establish an American branch of this organization. Its focus would be not only on war but also peacetime disasters, such as floods, earthquakes, and famines. In 1881, as result of her efforts, the American Red Cross became a reality.

10 This question has two parts. First, answer part A. Then, answer part B.

Part A

What can readers infer about Clara Barton based on the passage?

Ⓐ She hoped to become a doctor after the war.

Ⓑ She did everything she could to help others.

Ⓒ She enjoyed the excitement of battlefields.

Ⓓ She was quiet and preferred to be alone.

Part B

Which sentence(s) from the passage **best** supports the answer in part A?

Ⓐ Her talks about her experiences in the war were very popular.

Ⓑ She would not spend time trying to deal with situations that could not be improved.

Ⓒ No matter what was going on around her, Clara stayed calm and carried out her responsibilities.

Ⓓ Clara worked tirelessly at a total of 16 battle sites. She became known as the "angel of the battlefield."

Read the passage. Then answer the questions.

Meet Eleanor Roosevelt

In 1932, Franklin Roosevelt was elected president of the United States. His wife, Eleanor, told reporters in her practical, no-nonsense way, "There isn't going to be any First Lady. There is just going to be plain, ordinary Mrs. Roosevelt." She wanted people to respect her for her own accomplishments, not because she was the president's wife.

Eleanor Roosevelt was not ordinary, however. After she married Franklin Roosevelt in 1905, she became active in public service. During World War I, she worked for the American Red Cross. Then, in 1921, Franklin Roosevelt suffered a bout with a disease called polio that left him unable to walk. Because of his illness, his mother told him to retire from politics. Eleanor convinced him to continue.

Eleanor began helping Franklin with his political career, and she never stopped. After he became president, she gave press conferences and spoke out on behalf of many causes. These causes included human rights and children's issues. She helped the League of Women Voters, which encouraged women to take an active part in government. She gave radio broadcasts and wrote a daily newspaper column called "My Day," for which she earned more money than Franklin did as president. All of that was in addition to raising five children.

Eleanor focused a great deal of her energy on helping the poor and finding ways the government could help them. This was particularly important during the Great Depression, which lasted from 1929 to 1939. She also stood firmly against racial discrimination. She fought the unfair treatment of minorities whenever and wherever she could.

Because the First Lady was so involved in everything that went on, people called her the "legs and ears" of the president. Some people criticized her for being too involved in the government. After all, she was "only" the First Lady. Others wondered if she wanted to be president someday. She said that while she was not interested, many other women were worthy of the office. However, she added, "At this time, no woman can obtain and hold the support necessary for election."

Franklin's death in April 1945 didn't stop Eleanor, however. From 1945 until 1953, she worked for the United Nations. President Truman asked her to serve as the United States representative to the United Nations. She helped to write the UN's *Universal Declaration of Human Rights*. This document lists rights that people all over the world should have. Eleanor felt this document was her greatest achievement. Though she worked for the rights of all humans, she continued to focus on women's issues, as well. Because of her efforts, President John F. Kennedy appointed her chair of the Commission on the Status of Women. She held many important positions in her life. She traveled the world until her death in 1962.

Eleanor Roosevelt was once a shy, timid little girl who faced great suffering. Both her parents died when she was very young. Yet Eleanor overcame her fears and her hardships to become the "First Lady of the World." She said, "You gain strength, courage, and confidence by every experience in which you really stop to look fear in the face. You must do the thing you think you cannot do." No other First Lady of the United States has received as many awards and honors as she did. Though she has been gone many years, Eleanor Roosevelt continues to be one of the world's most admired women.

---

11 The author states, "Eleanor Roosevelt continues to be one of the world's most admired women." Which **two** details from the passage support the author's opinion?

Ⓐ She traveled the world until her death in 1962.

Ⓑ Both of her parents died when she was very young.

Ⓒ Others wondered if she wanted to be president someday.

Ⓓ She helped to write the UN's *Universal Declaration of Human Rights*.

Ⓔ Because of her efforts, President John F. Kennedy appointed her chair of the Commission on the Status of Women.

12 Read the sentence from the passage.

> President Truman asked her to <u>serve</u> as the United States representative to the United Nations.

What is the meaning of the word <u>serve</u> as it is used in the passage?

Ⓐ to wait on a table

Ⓑ to act as a servant

Ⓒ to be of definite use

Ⓓ to perform the duties of

13 The author uses the following quote from Eleanor Roosevelt in the passage.

> You gain strength, courage, and confidence by every experience in which you really stop to look fear in the face. You must do the thing you think you cannot do.

What is the meaning of the adage "stop to look fear in the face"?

Ⓐ work through your fears

Ⓑ back away from your fears

Ⓒ be honest about your fears

Ⓓ stop doing something if you have fears

Name _____   Date _____

14 This question has two parts. First, answer part A. Then, answer part B.

Part A

Read the paragraph from the passage.

> Eleanor focused a great deal of her energy on helping the poor and finding ways the government could help them. This was particularly important during the Great Depression, which lasted from 1929 to 1939. She also stood firmly against racial discrimination. She fought the unfair treatment of minorities whenever and wherever she could.

What does the word discrimination mean as it is used in the passage?

- Ⓐ wrongful behavior toward others
- Ⓑ inflexible attitude or opinion about others
- Ⓒ carefully formed belief about groups of people
- Ⓓ knowing what makes groups of people different

Part B

Which phrase from the passage **best** helps the reader understand the meaning of discrimination?

- Ⓐ stood firmly
- Ⓑ unfair treatment
- Ⓒ wherever she could
- Ⓓ particularly important

15 What is the main idea of the passage "Meet Eleanor Roosevelt"? Use key details from the text to support your answer.

_____

_____

_____

_____

Read the passage. Then answer the questions.

A Piece of the Past

On a warm spring day, Nate sat on a small mound of dirt in his backyard. He had been working outside all morning. He wiped the sweat off his forehead and ran his fingers through the soil. A few days ago, Nate's dad had suggested that they start a vegetable garden, and Nate had eagerly agreed. He enjoyed being out in the sun, and he loved the feel of the damp earth between his fingers. His father had bought several small tomato and squash plants to start their garden, and Nate was ready to get the project under way.

Nate's dad showed him how to handle each young seedling and how to prepare the soil. Nate began by using a trowel to turn over the earth. The deeper he dug, the cooler and damper the soil became. He pulled out a large stone, and then the small shovel hit something sharp. Nate carefully dug under the object and then excavated it from the dirt. It was small, black, and triangular. Nate rubbed off all the dirt and called, "Hey, Dad, I found something!"

"What is it?" asked his dad.

"I am not sure," Nate said, "but look here." Nate held out his open hand, and the sun glinted off the shiny black object. He was sure he'd seen something like it in one of his books at school, but he couldn't quite remember the name.

"Well, look at that," his dad said, whistling softly. He took the object and held it up to the sunlight. "It's an arrowhead," he said, "sending us a message from the past."

"A message from the past?" asked Nate.

"Yes," said his dad, "and it says that our ancestors hunted right here." Nate's family was part Comanche, and they lived in Kansas, where their ancestors had migrated.

"Arrowheads were used for hunting animals, right?" asked Nate.

"Yes, the Comanche used bows and arrows to hunt a variety of animals, including buffalo," his dad explained.

Name _____ Date _____

"Dad, did you ever hunt buffalo?" Nate asked.

"No, Son, of course not," Nate's dad said with a quiet laugh. "The buffalo had disappeared long before I was born."

Nate's dad went on to explain that the land where they lived was once inhabited by enormous buffalo herds. He told Nate that the Comanche had relied on the buffalo for meat and used the animals' hides for warmth. "No part of the buffalo was wasted," he said. As Nate listened, he imagined the huge buffalo stampeding in thunderous herds across the vast plains.

"Let's go inside for the day," his dad said. "It's been quite a memorable day. I'd say that we are off to a good start with our garden, and you found quite a treasure there!"

They gathered up their tools, and Nate brushed the dirt off his clothes. He couldn't wait to show the arrowhead to his friends and tell them what his dad had revealed about their ancestors. He knew they would be as excited as he was to actually hold a piece of the past. He was going to try to find that book, too, so he could learn even more about the arrowhead.

Nate took one last look at the arrowhead and then put it in his pocket. He and his dad walked inside, both of them lost in daydreams about the buffalo and the people of long ago.

---

16 Which of the following sentences from the passage contains an example of personification?

Ⓐ "The deeper he dug, the cooler and damper the soil became."

Ⓑ "Nate held out his open hand, and the sun glinted off the shiny black object."

Ⓒ "It's an arrowhead," he said, "sending us a message from the past."

Ⓓ "The buffalo had disappeared long before I was born."

Name _____ Date _____

17 What **two** messages are revealed when Nate finds the arrowhead?

    Ⓐ   that the soil was good for gardening

    Ⓑ   that Nate enjoyed working in the dirt

    Ⓒ   that Nate's ancestors once hunted there

    Ⓓ   that the Comanche had relied on the buffalo

    Ⓔ   that Nate should have paid more attention in school

18 Read the sentences from the story below. Underline the word that has a prefix with the meaning <u>outside</u> or <u>no longer</u>.

> The deeper he dug, the cooler and damper the soil became. He pulled out a large stone, and then the small shovel hit something sharp. Nate carefully dug under the object and then excavated it from the dirt. It was small, black, and triangular.

19 Read the paragraph from the story. Underline the **three** words in the paragraph below that have a similar meaning to the word <u>large</u>.

> Nate's dad went on to explain that the land where they lived was once inhabited by enormous buffalo herds. He told Nate that the Comanche had relied on the buffalo for meat and used the animals' hides for warmth. "No part of the buffalo was wasted," he said. As Nate listened, he imagined the huge buffalo stampeding in thunderous herds across the vast plains.

Name _____   Date _____

20 This question has two parts. First, answer part A. Then, answer part B.

Part A

From whose point of view is the passage "A Piece of the Past" told?

Ⓐ Nate

Ⓑ Nate's dad

Ⓒ a Comanche ancestor

Ⓓ a narrator who is not a character in the passage

Part B

Read the sentences from the passage.

> Nate's dad showed him how to handle each young seedling and how to prepare the soil. Nate began by using a trowel to turn over the earth. The deeper he dug, the cooler and damper the soil became. He pulled out a large stone, and then the small shovel hit something sharp.

Which words support your answer from part A?

Ⓐ he, the

Ⓑ him, he

Ⓒ dad, began

Ⓓ Nate, young

Name _____ Date _____

Writing

Read and answer each question.

21 Choose the sentence that contains a spelling error.

Ⓐ   We enjoyed watching the colorfull sunset.

Ⓑ   Chris was restless as he waited for his turn.

Ⓒ   Ella rode her bike across the smooth pavement.

Ⓓ   She earned extra points on the test for neatness.

22 Julio is writing a story for his class about a special event. He wants to revise his draft by combining short sentences using relative adverbs or pronouns. Read the draft of these sentences from his story and complete the task that follows.

> There is one day that will always stand out in my mind as being special. It changed my life forever. <u>That was the day. My baby brother was born.</u> Jonah makes me smile, and I know we will be best friends when he is older.

Which revision is correct for the underlined sentences?

Ⓐ   That was the day when my baby brother was born.

Ⓑ   That was the day which my baby brother was born.

Ⓒ   That was the day, on which my baby brother was born.

Ⓓ   That was the day, the day when my baby brother was born.

23 Which sentence has an error in grammar usage?

Ⓐ   "Put your math book on your desk," said Ms. Diaz.

Ⓑ   We added three-digit numbers during math class today.

Ⓒ   Chloe stood across Morgan in line as the class walked to lunch.

Ⓓ   "Will you finish your homework before dinner?" asked Aunt Sue.

Name _____ Date _____

24 Sofia is writing a story for her class about a camping trip. Read the draft of her paragraph and complete the task that follows.

> For Simon, the best part of any camping trip was the camp fire. He loved <u>having a fire at night</u>. Simon also enjoyed the smell of the burning wood and cooking hot dogs in the fire. Before the sun went down, he and his uncle collected broken tree limbs in the forest and carried them back to camp.

The writer wants to replace the underlined words to make her writing more descriptive. Which **three** phrases would be better choices?

Ⓐ to sit and watch the fire after dark

Ⓑ how the glowing orange flames lit the night

Ⓒ to make a big fire with wood he found around

Ⓓ to watch the bright flames dancing in the darkness

Ⓔ listening as the flames crackled like breaking glass

Ⓕ building a fire and watching the flames that came from it

25 Which sentence has an error in organization?

Ⓐ Some seeds did not receive enough water, so they did not sprout.

Ⓑ The tallest plant had a height of six inches, so it received enough sun and water.

Ⓒ The plants that were kept inside did not receive any sunlight, so they did not grow.

Ⓓ All of the seeds were planted in the same garden, so they had the same type of soil.

Name _____ Date _____

26 A student is writing a report about white-tailed deer. Read the draft of the paragraph and answer the question that follows.

> Does have babies in the spring. The fur of the babies is reddish-brown and has white spots. This helps them blend in with the forest around them and keeps them safe from bobcats, mountain lions, and other animals.

What is the **best** way to rewrite the first sentence of the paragraph?

Ⓐ Does, which are female deer, have baby deer, called fawns, in the spring.

Ⓑ Mother deer have small, baby deer at the beginning of the year.

Ⓒ A doe is a mother deer who has babies in May or June.

Ⓓ Does have fawns in the spring.

27 Gabby wrote this informational report for her science class. Read this paragraph from the report and the question that follows.

> (1) Different kinds of sharks have different shapes of teeth. The shape depends on what they eat. (2) Some sharks have wide, sharp teeth, for tearing apart their prey. (3) Sharks that live near the ocean floor have thick, flat teeth for crushing food. (4) Sharks can have as many as 3,000 teeth at a time.

Which sentence should be removed?

Ⓐ sentence 1

Ⓑ sentence 2

Ⓒ sentence 3

Ⓓ sentence 4

28 Doug wrote the following paragraph as part of a story. Underline the **two** words with spelling errors.

It started out as the perfect day for a picnik. The sun was shining, and there was a warm breeze. I helped Dad by packing fruit and water bottles in the basket. He got meat, cheese, and bread, and Mom packed a blanket for us to sit on. We hurried around the house to gather everything we would need. Our family was so happy about spending the day together that we did not notise the change in weather outside. The blue sky had grown dark as thick clouds collected above.

29 Terrell wrote this passage about playing with his friends. Read his passage and underline the **two** sentences that have adverb or adjective errors.

After school yesterday, my friends and I went to the playground for several hours. It was the warmer day in months, so we were happy to be able to play outside. First we raced to the swings, where I went higher than any of my friends. Next we ran to the slides. There are three slides, and the green one is the fastest, so we all took turns on that one. While we were on the slides, Jordan's mom picked him up, and we were all disappointed. He had to leave earliest than me.

Name _____ Date _____

30 Marisol wrote a story about the first day of school. Read the paragraph from Marisol's story. Then, rewrite the paragraph to be better organized. Be sure to include transition words and details to make the events clear.

A huge smile grew across my face! After getting off the bus, I walked to room 27, my new classroom. The sign on the classroom door said, "Welcome to Mr. Harper's Class!" Luis was in Mr. Harper's class last year, and I was hoping he would be my teacher, too! I was nervous as I wondered who my new teacher would be. My heart was beating so fast I thought it might pound its way out of my chest.

_____

_____

_____

_____

Name _____ Date _____

Listening

Listen to the presentation. Then answer the questions.

Earthquakes

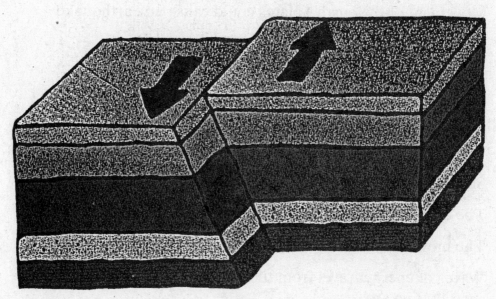

31 This question has two parts. First, answer part A. Then, answer part B.

Part A

What is the main idea of the passage?

- Ⓐ The earth is made of many layers.
- Ⓑ Earthquakes only last for a few minutes.
- Ⓒ The earth's outermost layer is called the crust.
- Ⓓ Movement of the earth's layers causes earthquakes.

Part B

Which detail **best** supports the answer to part A?

- Ⓐ The pieces of the earth's crust are known as plates.
- Ⓑ Seismic waves are waves of energy that have built up.
- Ⓒ Movement of the earth's plates causes pressure to build.
- Ⓓ The shaking of the earth lasts only a few minutes but feels longer.

32 Which **two** conclusions does the presentation support?

- Ⓐ Earthquakes can happen suddenly.
- Ⓑ Earthquakes are always destructive.
- Ⓒ The crust is the most important layer of the earth.
- Ⓓ Movement of the earth's plates could cause an earthquake at any time.
- Ⓔ The length of time an earthquake lasts is the same for every earthquake.

33 Which sentence explains what causes pressure to build on the rock below the earth's surface?

- Ⓐ Shifting plates make the rocks break up.
- Ⓑ The crust of the earth moves very slowly.
- Ⓒ The movement of the plates creates stress under the earth.
- Ⓓ Waves of energy travel from the broken rock through the surrounding area.

Listen to the presentation. Then answer the questions.

Animal Collectors

34 What is the main idea of the passage?

Ⓐ Many people collect valuable items.

Ⓑ Some animals collect and store food.

Ⓒ All animals store food in different ways.

Ⓓ Squirrels are the only animals that save nuts.

35 Which sentence supports the fact that "The squirrel makes hundreds of small hiding places for its nuts and seeds"?

Ⓐ The red squirrel builds a midden.

Ⓑ The gray squirrel uses scatter hoarding.

Ⓒ Red squirrels hide their food in a large pile.

Ⓓ Gray squirrels clean their food before hiding it.

36 This question has two parts. First, answer part A. Then, answer part B.

Part A

How are a red squirrel and a gray squirrel similar or different?

Ⓐ Both hide much of their food.

Ⓑ Gray squirrels build a large pile.

Ⓒ Both leave bits of shells behind.

Ⓓ Red squirrels carefully clean their food.

Part B

Which conclusion is **best** supported by the answer to part A?

Ⓐ All animals collect and store food.

Ⓑ Most animals eat nuts and pinecones.

Ⓒ Animals find most of their food in trees.

Ⓓ Animals collect and store food in different ways.

Listen to the presentation. Then answer the questions.

Why Are Trees Valuable?

37 Which **two** conclusions are supported by the presentation?

Ⓐ Many people benefit from trees.

Ⓑ Heat is the most important resource provided by trees.

Ⓒ Trees will continue to be important to people in the future.

Ⓓ Maple trees are more important than other types, since they provide syrup.

Ⓔ Homes are built from other materials, so trees are less valuable than in the past.

38 Many people have jobs that depend on trees. Which detail from the presentation **best** supports this conclusion?

Ⓐ Native Americans tapped maple trees for syrup and ate fruits and nuts from trees.

Ⓑ Trees also contribute to the health and beauty of our environment.

Ⓒ Then the trees are cut down and hauled to a lumber mill.

Ⓓ Today, trees continue to be a valuable resource.

39 What is the main idea of the passage?

Ⓐ Trees are a valuable resource.

Ⓑ Long ago, people depended on trees.

Ⓒ Many products we use today come from trees.

Ⓓ Animals depend on trees for a number of reasons.

Name _____ Date _____

Research

Read and answer each question.

40 A student is writing a report about echolocation. Read the sentences from the source and the directions that follow.

> Dolphins find their way in the ocean by making clicking sounds that send back echoes. This is called echolocation, a way to locate objects using sound. Dolphins use echolocation to help them catch fish to eat. The sounds that bounce off the fish let the dolphin know where the fish are.

The parts of the student's report are listed below. Choose **three** parts of the report where information from the source should be placed.

Ⓐ What is echolocation?

Ⓑ Echolocation in nature

Ⓒ Echolocation and humans

Ⓓ Using echolocation to find food

Ⓔ Experiments with echolocation

Ⓕ What we still need to learn about echolocation

41 A student has made a plan for research. It includes this research question: Why do chameleons change colors? Which of these is the **best** source for the information needed to answer the research question?

Ⓐ *Reptiles*

a book about different types of reptiles

Ⓑ www.chameleons101.com

a website with information about chameleons

Ⓒ "Lizards as Pets"

a magazine article about having a lizard as a household pet

Ⓓ "Reptiles from Around the World"

a magazine article with information about different reptiles from each continent

Name _____ Date _____

42 A student is planning a report about plants. The report will need to include several parts. Based on the information in the source below, identify **three** parts that could be included in the report.

> Table of Contents
>
> Chapter 1 Parts of a Plant
>
> Chapter 2 Functions of Each Plant Part
>
> Chapter 3 Plants as Food
>
> Chapter 4 Plants as Medicine
>
> Chapter 5 Poisonous Plants

  Ⓐ Where Plants Live

  Ⓑ Humans Need Plants

  Ⓒ Plants That Eat Insects

  Ⓓ Plants in the Rainforest

  Ⓔ Plant Parts and Their Jobs

  Ⓕ Plants to Stay Away From

43 A student is writing a research report about dog breeds. Here is the first draft. Underline the sentence that should not be in a research report.

> There are over 163 recognized breeds of dogs. Different breeds of dogs are unique in some way, making them the perfect pet for different owners. My favorite type of dog is a husky. Some dogs would love to play fetch for hours. Some dogs are high maintenance, and some dogs barely need a thing.

Name _____ Date _____

44 A student is writing a research report on volleyball equipment. She finds the following paragraph in an article. Underline the sentence that she could best use in her report.

Volleyball is a sport played by men and women. There are 6 players on each side of the court at one time. There is a net that is 7 feet high dividing the court in half. Players can hit the ball 3 times on each side. Games are played to 25 points.

Performance Task 3
Part 1

Giving Others a Helping Hand

Task:

You have been asked to write an article for the school newspaper explaining how philanthropy, which means helping other people by giving time and money, can make communities stronger. Your teacher has asked you to find three different sources about how people can help others. The first source is taken from history. The second source is about a project that took place in your own community a few years ago. The third is from a website.

After you have reviewed these sources, you will answer some questions about them. Briefly scan the sources and the three questions that follow. Then, go back and read the sources carefully so you will have the information you will need to answer the questions and complete your research. You may use scratch paper to take notes on the information you find in the sources as you read.

In Part 2, you will write an informational article using information you have read.

Directions for Beginning:

You will now review several sources. You can review any of the sources as often as you like.

Research Questions:

After reviewing the research sources, use the rest of the time in Part 1 to answer three questions about them. Your answers to these questions will be scored. Also, your answers will help you think about the information you have read, which should help you write your informational article.

You may refer back to your scratch paper to review your notes when you think it would be helpful. Answer the questions in the spaces below the items.

Your written notes on scratch paper will be available to you in Part 1 and Part 2 of the performance task.

Part 1

Source #1

You found an article in a history book about Andrew Carnegie, who used his success to help found public libraries in the nineteenth century.

The Man Who Built Libraries

Andrew Carnegie was born in Dunfermline, Scotland, in 1835. When he was 13, his family moved to the United States in search of a better life. The Carnegie family settled in Allegheny, Pennsylvania. This was a factory town just outside Pittsburgh. Andrew got a job working in a cotton mill. This was his first job, but he wouldn't work there long. He was destined to get better jobs, always making more money with more responsibilities.

A year later, Carnegie became a messenger in a telegraph office. Before long, Carnegie was promoted to telegraph operator. Two years later, he became a company leader. He was on his way up.

Carnegie saved the money he earned so he could start his own business. At age 35, he opened his first steel mill. Steel was an important building material. Carnegie's mill made him one of the wealthiest people in the United States. When he turned 65, Carnegie sold the steel company for $480 million. Now that he had so much money, he wanted to do something for other people. He became a philanthropist, someone who gives time and money to help people have better lives.

In 1881, Carnegie sent a letter to the city of Pittsburgh. If the city would provide the land and promise to maintain the library, he would provide the money to build a free library. Carnegie also opened four other libraries in towns where he had owned steel mills.

Soon, many communities asked for libraries, so Carnegie made a plan for funding new libraries. He no longer paid for everything. Instead, he gave money to construct the building while the community provided the land and raised funds to support the library. He also asked communities to promise that they would never charge fees to library users. His plan worked. New libraries were built all over the country this way.

Name _____ Date _____

Carnegie helped create something that has lasted long after his death. He made the public library an important part of every community. Today, libraries provide many services. People can use computers to research jobs or colleges. Students can receive help with their homework from tutors. New immigrants can take classes in English, and people of all ages and backgrounds can borrow books, music, and films for absolutely free. This is exactly how Carnegie had imagined it should be.

Source #2

You found an article in a local magazine about a community garden that was founded in your own community several years ago.

A Garden Grows

Every day on his walk to and from school, Mateo Ramirez passed a big lot at the corner of Fourth Street and Smith Lane. He wondered who owned it and why the owner didn't do something with the property. The lot was empty except for weeds, trash, and broken glass. Mateo worried that the land was being wasted. It seemed to be growing trash. But he did more than worry. He also began to form a plan that would bring about a great change in his community. We can all learn from his idea and actions, and make similar improvements in our own communities.

His plan came to him in school one day when his social studies teacher talked about the environment. It was decided that his social studies class was going to complete a project about the environment. That's when Mateo had a brainstorm. "I think we should organize a day to clean up the lot," he told his classmates.

Their social studies teacher, Mr. Chu, thought it was a wonderful idea, but he asked the students to do some research before they got started.

The class had to find out who owned the lot. Then they had to ask for permission to clean it up. On a field trip to city hall, the students learned that Madge Green was the owner. Madge Green was a wealthy woman, but she had never done anything with the lot.

Back at school, Mateo wrote Madge Green a letter. He asked if she would let the community take care of the lot. Another student, Ben Garza, suggested taking pictures of the lot.

Within a week, the class received an answer. "Those pictures made me so sad. I'm 90, so I don't get around as much as I used to," Mrs. Green wrote in her letter. "I'd be thrilled if you cleaned up the lot."

On March 26, the cleanup began. The students, along with families and friends, gathered at the lot. Everyone helped to pick up trash. At the end of the day, the workers stepped back to look at their work. "The lot is clean, but it looks really empty," Mateo said.

He had another idea. Maybe Madge Green would let them use the lot for a community garden. People from the neighborhood could pay a small fee to rent garden space. The money would buy fencing, topsoil, seeds, and other supplies for the garden. Mateo wrote to Madge Green with his new idea. He enclosed pictures of the cleaned up lot, too. Madge Green agreed.

In April, Mateo and Ben planted the first seeds in the community garden. During the summer, the neighborhood raised 20 pounds of beans, 50 pounds of corn, and over a 100 pounds of tomatoes. They gave some of these crops to a local food bank so hungry people could eat. The garden has become an important part of the community, and it continues to produce food for all every year. Anyone interested in starting a community garden can learn from Mateo's success.

Source #3
You found the following information on a website about famous women. This woman used her money to help change the world.

Mabel Dodge Luhan

Mabel was born in 1879. Her parents were very wealthy. At that time, young girls were not expected to do anything but learn how to be ladies. Rich young ladies usually married men who were also rich. Mabel got a good education, and she traveled all over the world. This was thought to make women better companions for their husbands.

Mabel married a young man whose family owned a steamship company. They were very happy for a few years, but when she was only 23 years old, her husband died. Now she was left on her own, but she was also very rich. She was not a very happy person for many years. In order to help her, her parents suggested she travel to Europe. After several years, she married again, and her second husband was also very rich.

When she returned to the United States, Mabel became interested in the arts. She had a lot of money, and artists usually didn't. She discovered one thing that made her feel better was to help other people. She enjoyed nice paintings, good music, and intelligent conversations. She decided to help people who were also interested in these things but could not afford to create them.

She opened up her home for artists to show their work without charge. This gave the artists public attention, allowing many artists to sell their paintings and make money. She also let writers live free in the upstairs of her large house. Many writers do not make any money. It takes a long time to write a book that makes money, and writers have to live somewhere in the meantime. She let them live in her house so they didn't have to worry about making money; they could just write.

But she did more than help artists. She was interested in helping people get a good education, too. Getting a good education meant going to a good university, and this took money. Many people who were intelligent enough to go to these schools simply couldn't afford to pay the tuition. She became friends with the Gibbs family. Their son was very smart, but they were not rich. Mabel paid for him to go to a very good university, where he graduated at the top of his class. After he graduated, he became an engineer. One of his first jobs was to design the setup for the lights on the Bay Bridge in San Francisco.

Mabel lived to be 83 years old. She did a lot of good for artists of all kinds. Every time you see the lights on the Bay Bridge, it is because of the good deeds of Mabel Dodge Luhan. She took her money and helped others, making the world a better and brighter place. Her good works shine on.

Name _____ Date _____

1 "The Man Who Built Libraries" focuses on a single individual and how he improved communities. Which individual in "A Garden Grows" stands out more than others? Why? What does this individual do that affects the community? Use **two** details from the source to support your answer.

_____

_____

_____

_____

2 What role does money play in these sources? How does it help philanthropists accomplish their goals? Choose **two** of the sources, and use **one** detail from **each** to support your answer.

_____

_____

_____

_____

Name _____ Date _____

3 Mark the boxes to match each source with the idea or ideas that it supports. A source may have more than one idea, and an idea may apply to more than one source.

	Source #1: The Man Who Built Libraries	Source #2: A Garden Grows	Source #3: Mabel Dodge Luhan
Success is best when it is shared with others.			
Many hands make light work.			
One individual can make a big difference.			
Those who have resources can help others.			
Something that is forgotten can become an important resource with the right care.			

125

Part 2

You will now review your notes and sources, and plan, draft, revise, and edit your writing. You may use your notes and go back to the sources. Now read your assignment and the information about how your writing will be scored, then begin your work.

Your Assignment

Your teacher wants you to write an article for the school newspaper explaining why philanthropy is important to communities. You decide you will write about how individuals can contribute to their communities and what happens when people help others. Your article will be read by other students, teachers, and parents.

Using more than one source, develop a main idea about how philanthropy helps communities. Choose the most important information from more than one source to support your main idea. Then, write an informational article about your main idea that is several paragraphs long. Clearly organize your article, and support your main idea with details from the sources. Use your own words except when quoting directly from the sources. Be sure to give the source title or number when using details from the sources.

REMEMBER: A well-written informational article

- has a clear main idea.
- is well-organized and stays on the topic.
- has an introduction and a conclusion.
- uses transitions.
- uses details from the sources to support your main idea.
- puts the information from the sources in your own words, except when using direct quotations from the sources.
- gives the title or number of the source for the details or facts you included.
- develops ideas clearly.
- uses clear language.
- follows rules of writing (spelling, punctuation, and grammar usage).

Now begin work on your informational article. Manage your time carefully so that you can

    1. plan your informational article.

    2. write your informational article.

    3. revise and edit the final draft of your informational article.

For Part 2, you are being asked to write an informational article that is several paragraphs long. Write your response in the space below.

Remember to check your notes and your prewriting and planning as you write and then revise and edit your informational article.

_____

_____

_____

_____

_____

_____

_____

_____

_____

_____

Name _____ Date _____

_____

_____

_____

_____

_____

_____

_____

_____

_____

_____

_____

_____

_____

_____

_____

_____

_____

Name _____ Date _____

_____

_____

_____

_____

_____

_____

_____

_____

_____

_____

_____

_____

_____

_____

_____

_____

_____

_____

_____